# THE WISCONSIN
# TRAVELER'S
# *Companion*

# A GUIDE TO COUNTRY SIGHTS

BY JERRY APPS
WITH ILLUSTRATIONS BY JULIE SUTTER-BLAIR

WISCONSIN TRAILS
MADISON, WISCONSIN

First edition, first printing

Text copyright © 1997 Jerold W. Apps
Illustrations copyright © 1997 Julie Sutter-Blair

Library of Congress Catalog Card Number: 97-60686
ISBN: 0-915024-56-X

Editor: Elizabeth McBride
Designer: Kathie Campbell
Printed in the United States of America by Master Litho.

Wisconsin Tales and Trails Inc.
P.O. Box 5650
Madison, WI 53705
(800) 236-8088

*To those who*
*explore country roads.*

# TABLE OF CONTENTS

# The Landscape

# THE LANDSCAPE

Wisconsin is a diverse state. We have forests and farmfields, hills and plains, cows and emus, alfalfa and cranberries. This book is designed to help you identify what you see as you travel around the countryside. It will also answer some of your questions. Why is Wisconsin a dairy state? Why does it contain more silos than any other state in the nation? Why are there steep hills in the southwest, and flatlands in the central region? Why did various ethnic groups settle here?

We begin with a discussion of the landscape, which, of course, underlies almost every other feature of Wisconsin. To understand the landscape, we must track the movement of the glaciers.

## The Wisconsin Glacier

The last glacier to descend into Wisconsin originated east of Hudson's Bay in Canada, arriving here some 25,000 years ago. The animals and birds disappeared; trees and other vegetation were obliterated. Much of Wisconsin became an icy wilderness, buried under hundreds of tons of ice that slowly moved southward, sometimes only a few feet a year but other times by as much as 200 or 300 feet.

Glaciers are made from the accumulation of compacted snow, which enlarges each year more rapidly than it melts. They advance by the force of gravity, but they also move under the pressure of their own weight, slowly but relentlessly. Glaciers crush, shear or bury almost all obstacles in their path, sometimes picking up boulders and gravel, which they carry along with them.

Talk to any farm boy who grew up in a glaciated part of Wisconsin, and you'll learn firsthand how the glaciers affected the state. He'll tell you about the stones he had to pick every spring before the crops could be planted—stones that had traveled along with the glacier and were deposited far from their point of origin when the ice melted. Some were the size of softballs, but many weighed more than the boy. "The frost brings them up," his father had told him. And his father was right, for the yearly freezing and thawing of the land moved the buried fieldstones to the surface as surely as the geese fly north and the oaks leaf out each spring.

In northern and eastern Wisconsin you'll find stones of every color and shape. When settlers arrived in Wisconsin, the stones were both cursed, because they were always in the way, and praised, because they made for a sturdy building material. Today you'll see fieldstones lining cultivated fields. You can see them, too, in dairy barn walls, in church foundations, in pump houses, hog shelters, in the cellar walls of many older rural homes and, sometimes, in silos. Occasionally, you will see them in cattle pastures, remaining as the glacier left them thousands of years ago.

The glaciers also formed hills and ridges, created thousands of lakes, and left behind rich soils in north-central, eastern and southeastern Wisconsin.

When the last Wisconsin glacier reached the region around the present-day city of Superior, it flowed into a crack in the earth's crust and scoured out Lake Superior. When the glacier reached present-day Door County, it was deflected by a hard rock outcropping called the Niagara Escarpment. This escarpment forms the Door Peninsula and continues east, eventually ending at Niagara Falls. The Niagara Escarpment also runs south along the east side of Lake Winnebago to south of present-day Fond du Lac. One of the most obvious places to see the Niagara Escarpment is east of Fond du Lac on

*Advance of the last glacier*

# THE LANDSCAPE

Highway 23. The steep hill you encounter as you leave the city is the escarpment.

The escarpment split the glacier and created a new "lobe," called the Green Bay Lobe. This lobe moved west and south, scooped out Green Bay and Lake Winnebago, and created what is now Horicon Marsh. Along the way it dug out Green Lake, the deepest inland lake in Wisconsin.

The Green Bay Lobe stopped its southerly movement at Rock County. The low line of hills east of Interstate 39 (visible as you travel from Westfield to Stevens Point), the Baraboo Bluffs near Baraboo and the rolling hills west of Madison all mark the spot where the glacier stopped its westward expansion.

As the glacial ice melted, a huge lake formed in central Wisconsin, stretching from the Baraboo Bluffs north to Stevens Point and west to Tomah and Eau Claire. The bluffs acted as a dam, and as the volume of water increased, the area covered by the lake

*sandstone pillars*

*Niagara Escarpment*

grew larger. Mill Bluff State Park, near Camp Douglas, contains examples of sandstone pillars that once were islands in this lake, shaped by wave action. Another sandstone pillar is found a few miles west of Coloma, on Highway 21.

About 14,000 years ago, the waters of Glacial Lake Wisconsin finally began cutting through the sandstone rocks that held them back. The lake drained. In the process, the surging water gorged out the dells of the Wisconsin River, leaving exotic rock formations now enjoyed by thousands of visitors each year.

After the lake drained, a huge, flat, sandy lake bed was left behind. For many years, these lands were considered nearly worthless. Scrub oak and jack pine grew here but little else. There never seemed to be enough rainfall to support corn, alfalfa or other agricultural crops. Enter irrigation. Researchers discovered that a few feet beneath the sandy surface of the old lake bed lay millions of gallons of water. The

Kettle lake

Drumlin

# THE LANDSCAPE

University of Wisconsin College of Agriculture Hancock Experimental Station began pumping it out and spraying it on crops. Today, this old lake bed is one of the richest vegetable growing areas in the United States.

As the glacier receded, it also left behind an array of interestingly shaped hills, especially in the counties southeast of Lake Winnebago. Called drumlins, they look like the bowls of overturned spoons and are anywhere from 200 feet to two miles long. You can see drumlins especially well in the Kettle Moraine State Forest and in Dodge and its neighboring counties. The State Capitol in Madison sits on a drumlin.

As the glacier melted, huge blocks of ice sometimes broke off and were buried in rock and gravel. When these blocks melted, lakes formed. Today they are referred to as "kettle" lakes because they resemble the shape of a kettle. The Kettle Moraine State Forest is a good place to see them.

## The Driftless Area

A vast region that includes southwestern Wisconsin and parts of eastern Iowa, southwestern Minnesota and northwestern Illinois was not touched by this glacier. This region is called the Driftless Area because it contains no glacial rock debris or "drift." It covers 15,000 square miles. Wisconsin's portion is about 180 miles long and 120 miles wide.

The landscape of the Driftless Area is vastly different from the glaciated region that surrounds it. Much of it consists of rugged hills, most of them steeper than those in the glaciated region. (Exceptions are the high rock outcroppings too hard for the glacier to destroy, such as Rib Mountain near Wausau.) There are almost no natural lakes.

The area does contain several caves, of which the most well-known is Cave of the Mounds, near Blue Mounds. Caves are generally formed by the action of underground rivers; any caves that may have existed in Wisconsin's glaciated region collapsed under the glacier's weight or were destroyed by its movement.

The is how Edward Daniels, Wisconsin's first state geologist, described southwestern

Wisconsin in 1854: "About one-third of the surface is prairie, dotted and belted with beautiful groves and oak-openings. The scenery combines every element of beauty and grandeur—giving us the sunlit prairie, with its soft swell, waving grass and thousand flowers, the sombre depths of primeval forests; and castellated cliffs, rising hundreds of feet, with beetling crags which a Titan might have piled his fortress." Today's travelers consider the Driftless Area to be one of the most beautiful parts of the state.

Soils in the driftless region are generally fertile but often hard to work because of the hills. To prevent soil erosion, always a problem when steep slopes are cultivated, farmers developed a couple of special techniques. They laid out their fields on the contours, a practice called "contour farming." And they planted crops on the long, sloping hillsides in strips a hundred or so yards wide—first a strip of corn, then a strip of alfalfa, another strip of corn and so on. This is called "strip cropping." Traveling through the Driftless Area in summer, especially in Grant, Lafayette, Iowa, Richland, Crawford and Vernon counties, you'll see acre upon acre of contour strip crops wrapping around the hills, creating beautiful patterns and colors. In spring, the brown of freshly turned earth contrasts with the green of new alfalfa. In midsummer, rows of corn contrast with carpetlike hayfields. In fall, tan-colored ripening corn stands out against deep green alfalfa and the multihued oak trees on the ridges above the fields.

*contour strip crops*

# THE LANDSCAPE

## Lakes and Rivers

Also legacies of the glacier are more than 15,000 lakes and an intricate system of rivers and streams. Today, water makes up about a million acres, or almost 3 percent, of the state's surface.

The French explorers and fur traders used Wisconsin's waterways extensively. One of the most famous water highways in the state is the Fox-Wisconsin river route. The Fox River begins east of Portage in central Wisconsin, then flows northeastward to Green Bay, the Great Lakes system and into the St. Lawrence River. The Wisconsin River begins in northern Wisconsin and flows due south until it reaches Portage. It then veers west and flows into the Mississippi River at Prairie du Chien. What is most interesting about these two rivers is that they flow in opposite directions and yet come within a mile and a half of each other on a flat, swampy plain. Indians living in the

Major Wisconsin rivers

region were long familiar with this water route. They either portaged their canoes or floated them across the swamp during high water. As early as 1766, a small ditch was dug between the two rivers so canoes could easily float from one river to the other. Following the lead of the Indians, French explorers and fur traders began following this historic river route. Thus, early Wisconsin history begins in Green Bay, the eastern end of the route, and in Prairie du Chien, the western end.

Portage, the town where the two rivers came closest, also has a long, rich history. In 1849, the United States government began building a canal in Portage. (You can still see remnants of the canal today.) By 1856, it was possible to travel by small steamboat from Green Bay to Prairie du Chien.

When you visit today's Omro and Berlin, Princeton and Montello, imagine steamboats going through on their way to the canal at Portage. The Fox River is only several yards wide in these cities, just wide enough for those small boats.

Wisconsin's rivers were important not only for transportation but for industry. When settlers from New England and New York arrived beginning in the 1840s, followed by thousands of European immigrants, rivers and streams provided water power to run flour and saw mills.

## First Inhabitants

Native people lived for thousands of years in what is now Wisconsin before the first white person arrived. Today, about 40,000 American Indians live in the state, about 10,000 on reservations.

Wisconsin is reminded of its Indian heritage in many ways. The word "Wisconsin" comes from the Indian word *Meskousing*, which refers to the great river that runs through the state. There is no agreement on the tribe from which this word originated, but authorities do agree that it means "where the waters gather." The French spelled the word "Ouisconsin." The English spelled it many ways, finally settling on "Wisconsin."

*Indian tribes in the 1800s*

CHIPPEWA

Sioux

MENOMINEE

WINNEBAGO

*Southern Chippewa, Ottawa & Potawatomi*

Many of Wisconsin's counties, cities and villages have Indian names. These include Oneida, Menominee, Winnebago, Waushara, Waupaca, Outagamie, Chippewa and Ozaukee counties and the cities of Wautoma, Wausau, Ojibwa, Odanah, Okauchee, Oconomowoc, Oshkosh, Shawano and Mazomanie.

Wisconsin's Indians knew about maple syrup and how to harvest cranberries and prepare them for food. They also annually harvested wild rice, which grew in the

# THE LANDSCAPE

marshes and along the lake edges in northern Wisconsin. Early settlers learned about these crops from their Indian neighbors.

Indian mounds are another reminder of the state's Indian heritage. About a thousand years ago, mound-building Indians left behind effigy mounds that usually depicted mammals, birds or reptiles. Indian mounds may be seen at Devil's Lake State Park, Governor Nelson State Park, High Cliff State Park, Lizard Mound State Park, Perrot State Park, Wyalusing State Park and Indian Mound Park in Sheboygan, on the University of Wisconsin-Madison campus and in many other locations.

Aztalan State Park near Lake Mills is the site of a stockade built by Indians who lived there between 1100 and 1300 A.D. Their village included 21 acres enclosed by a stockade with 12-foot-high log walls. Within the walls were rectangular and circular dwellings and pyramidlike structures.

Compared to residents of other states, Wisconsin's settlers got along reasonably well with the Indians. The Black Hawk War of 1832 was an exception. In violation of a treaty, Chief Black Hawk, in that year, led about a thousand warriors, old men, women and children across the Mississippi River into Illinois. Unknown to the Indian leader, militia and army regulars under the command of General Henry Atkinson (Fort Atkinson is named after him) learned about the treaty violation and began pursuing the Indians. Abraham Lincoln of Illinois was a part of the military group.

Chief Black Hawk and his people traveled up the Rock River into Wisconsin and, at Lake Koshkonong, turned west, traveling through what would become Madison, and crossed the Wisconsin River near present-day Sauk City. Several skirmishes occurred along the way, including the Battle of Wisconsin Heights near the Wisconsin River. Several times Chief Black Hawk tried to surrender, but the military would not agree and persisted in their pursuit.

The tired and bedraggled Indians continued toward the Mississippi River, arriving there Aug. 1, 1832. They quickly fashioned makeshift rafts, and a few of the band managed to cross into Iowa. Unfortunately for the Indians, an armed military boat, the

Warrior, was coming downstream. Once again Black Hawk tried to surrender, but he was ignored. With the Warrior facing them on the river and the army behind them, 150 Indians were killed, another 150 drowned and about 50 were captured, including Black Hawk. The scrimmage became known as the Battle of Bad Axe, after a river that entered the Mississippi at this point. The village of Victory is near the site of this final battle; a few miles east you'll find the village of Retreat.

## French in Wisconsin

The first white people in Wisconsin were French; they lived in the state for more than 150 years before other ethnic groups arrived. Jean Nicolet, a French explorer, reached what is now Wisconsin in 1634. He, with his Indian guides and canoes, pulled ashore north of the present-day city of Green Bay at a place called Red Banks, a site of a major Winnebago Indian village. (A plaque depicting this historic event can be seen alongside Highway 57 near Dyckesville.) Legend has it that when Nicolet stepped on shore he shot off his pistols, scaring the wits out of the Indians who were there to greet him.

Nicolet saw a vast land of rapidly flowing rivers and a forest of white pine, hemlock, tamarack, balsam fir and spruce that stretched from central Wisconsin to Lake Superior. In eastern Wisconsin, oaks and maples were interspersed with open prairies. In southern Wisconsin grew giant bur oaks, with corky thick bark that resisted the wildfires that raced across the grassy prairies nearly every spring. But mostly in the south and southwest were prairies, thousands upon thousands of acres of rich soil where big and little bluestem grasses and wildflowers grew.

Nicolet was followed by other Frenchmen who traveled throughout the region, trading with the Indians for furs. French missionaries followed the fur traders. Although attempts to convert the Indians to Christianity were often futile, the missionaries had considerable influence on what was to become Wisconsin. They established permanent settlements, and they traveled a great deal. In 1663, Jesuit Claude Allouez was named vicar of what is now known as the Middle West. The base of his operations, in 1665,

# THE LANDSCAPE

was La Pointe du Saint Esprit, near present-day Ashland. In 1669, Allouez moved to the Green Bay area and began working with the Indian tribes along the upper Fox River. In the winter of 1671-72, Allouez and Father Louis Andre built the first permanent mission house on the Fox River at De Pere. French interest in exploring the mighty Mississippi River led Father Marquette and Louis Jolliet, a young fur trader, to canoe down the Fox River, portage the mile and a half to the Wisconsin River and then paddle on to the Mississippi. They reached the Mississippi on June 17, 1673, and are credited with being the first white men to see the river and note that it flowed south rather than north, as some had speculated. Nicholas Perrot, another fur trader, is credited with being the first white man to discover lead mines in Wisconsin and Iowa, in 1690.

Today's Wisconsin has many reminders of French explorers, especially in place names, such as Fond du Lac, Butte des Morts, Prairie du Chien, La Baye, Eau Claire, Trempealeau, La Valle, La Farge, Nicolet, Perrot, Marquette, Montreal, St. Croix Falls, Lac du Flambeau, Allouez, La Crosse and Lac Court Oreilles.

## The Northwest Ordinances of 1785 and 1787

The region from Ohio to the Mississippi River was defined as the "Northwest." The Northwest Ordinance of 1785 created a survey system that allowed for easy buying and selling of land in this region, and for developing accurate maps. It placed a grid of straight lines running north, south, east and west on the countryside. Today, flying over Wisconsin, it is easy to see the results of the survey in the rectangular fields and straight roads. The survey also established townships 6 miles square and divided them into 36 sections, each 1 mile square or 640 acres. The sections were further divided into quarter sections of 160 acres each, and each of them into 40-acre blocks. Using this system, any piece of land could be legally and accurately identified.

Wisconsin was not surveyed from Lake Michigan west, as one might think. Rather, the survey began at the Fourth Principal Meridian, a survey line extending north from the Illinois border. (The Fourth Principal Meridian forms the present boundary between Grant County on the west and Iowa and Lafayette counties on the east). From there, the survey proceeded east to Lake Michigan and west to the Mississippi River.

The Northwest Ordinance of 1787 stipulated that the region was to go through various stages of development and eventually be divided into no fewer than three and no more than five states. Eventually, five states, beginning with Ohio in 1803, then Indiana, Illinois, Michigan and, in 1848, Wisconsin, were carved out of the territory.

## Lead Mining

Until the 1820s, Indians claimed Wisconsin, except for small white settlements at Green Bay, Milwaukee, Portage and Prairie du Chien, and the beginnings of a lead mining settlement near the Mississippi River in the southwest.

Lead diggings

In this latter region, Indians had mined lead themselves since the middle of the 18th century. They used the lead for ornaments and, after they acquired firearms, to make shot. In the mid-1820s, white lead miners poured into the area. Lead was widely used by the military for cannonballs and musket bullets. It was also important to settlers as they moved west across the country. Lead bullets put venison, wild turkey, squirrel and rabbit meat on the table. Lead bullets also dispatched marauding bears that killed farm animals.

By 1830, when Wisconsin was still part of Michigan Territory, the number of settlers was increasing rapidly, and most were lead miners. Mineral Point, in the midst of lead

# THE LANDSCAPE

mining country, boasted 500 inhabitants in 1830. In that year, the lead mining region contained half of the white population of what was to become Wisconsin. The earliest arriving miners came up the Mississippi River from the South, but in the mid-1830s, miners from Cornwall immigrated in large numbers. By 1840, Wisconsin Territory was producing 31 million pounds of lead, more than half of all the lead mined in the country.

Today, as you travel in southwestern Wisconsin, you can spot many reminders of the lead mining era. Look for closed mine sites and notice village and city names that recall the mining days: Mineral Point, New Diggings and Lead Mine are examples. If you stop in Mineral Point, you can feast on pasties, a meat pie that Cornish miners carried with them to the mines, and you can tour a once-working lead mine. Historians believe that Wisconsin takes its nickname, the "Badger State," from these early lead miners, who lived in holes in the riverbanks, like badgers.

## Agricultural Settlers

Between 1833 and 1848, a series of treaties with various Indian tribes opened up lands for settlement. In 1834, when Wisconsin was still part of Michigan Territory, land offices opened at Green Bay and Mineral Point, and between 1835 and 1838, much of the region was surveyed. Wisconsin was ready for settlement.

Many early settlers came from New York, but a number of others arrived from Ohio, Pennsylvania, Vermont and other Eastern states. These settlers were called Yankees. They were primarily farmers who moved west to make their fortunes, or so they hoped, on Wisconsin's fertile, undisturbed soils.

The Easterners stayed in Wisconsin. Many place names are credited to them: Brooklyn, Almond, Sharon, Seneca, Rochester and Wild Rose are all derived from New York place names. The town of Rutland in Dane County is named after Rutland, Vermont.

## Early Black Settlers

Free and escaped slaves settled in Wisconsin. A few lead miners from Southern states brought their black slaves with them, but escaped slaves also arrived by way of the Underground Railroad. History records that in the early 1840s, free blacks came to Calumet County and founded Chilton. A black man is also credited with establishing the Township of Freedom in Outagamie County. The 1850 Wisconsin census listed 635 free blacks and no slaves. Ten years later, the number of free blacks had climbed to 1,171.

By 1870 two black rural communities had been established in Wisconsin. One was called Pleasant Ridge and was near Lancaster in Grant County, and the other was Cheyenne Valley in northeastern Vernon County. Both were created by freed and escaped slaves, and both were farming communities. These black settlers got along well with their white neighbors; in fact, an integrated one-room country school operated in the Pleasant Ridge community. Over the years, however, members of both these communities dispersed.

## Immigrant Settlers

Starting in the 1840s, immigrants began arriving in Wisconsin from Germany, Norway, Denmark, Sweden, Ireland, Belgium, Holland, Switzerland, Wales, Czechoslovakia, Yugoslavia, Russia, Luxembourg, Finland, Italy, Poland and other European countries. They came for several reasons. With a lowering of the death rate in much of Europe due to medical and sanitary advances, population began to increase. Soon countries like Norway had more people than the land could accommodate.

In Germany, industrialization, an increase in the birth rate, a potato blight and other crop failures between 1846 and 1853 produced thousands of dispossessed farmers who looked to the United States for a new life. German immigrants were also interested in religious and political freedom—scarce commodities in Germany at that time. Wisconsin's climate was similar to that of Germany and northern Europe. Moreover, such a northerly climate was considered healthy. Early immigrants sent home letters encouraging their relatives to join them, and many did.

# THE LANDSCAPE

But why Wisconsin and not other states? To be sure, northern European immigrants did settle in other areas, especially the other Midwestern states: Iowa, Minnesota, Illinois, Ohio and Michigan. But Wisconsin had a special attraction. One practical reason was good transportation routes. Early immigrant groups spent, on average, 44 days crossing the wind-swept Atlantic on wave-tossed sailing vessels. Upon arrival in New York, many took river boats up the Hudson and then transferred to canal boats on the Erie Canal. Upon arrival in Buffalo, New York, they climbed aboard sailing vessels for the trip around Michigan to the Wisconsin ports of Sheboygan, Manitowoc and, especially, Milwaukee. Others took the Chicago Wagon Trail from Detroit to Chicago, and then traveled on to Wisconsin.

Another reason why immigrants chose to settle here is that Wisconsin actively encouraged it. In 1852, the Legislature established a Commissioner of Emigration, with an office in New York. In 1853, another law added a traveling agent who was to make sure that the Eastern newspapers knew of Wisconsin's natural resources and other great attributes.

Soon Germans became the largest immigrant group in the state. The climate was to their liking and farmland was readily available. The first few thousand formed communities, which others quickly joined when they arrived. The major area of German settlement was centered in Milwaukee, Ozaukee, Sheboygan, Manitowoc, Calumet and Dodge counties in eastern Wisconsin. By 1850, 12 percent of Wisconsin's population was German.

Germans contributed much to the state. They brought their taste for beer and the skills for brewing it. At one time nearly every Wisconsin community had a brewery with its *brau meister*. The names Pabst, Schlitz, Rahr, Blatz, Leinenkugel, Heileman, Gettleman and Miller soon became associated with Wisconsin's beer-making industry. Many former brewery buildings still stand in communities throughout the state.

Numerous Wisconsin restaurants and delis today regularly offer German foods: sauerkraut, bratwurst, cole slaw, dill pickles, potato salad, sour meats, noodles, cheesecake, poppyseed rolls, pretzels, coffee cake and caraway rye bread, to mention a few. Germans also brought their love for the land, their farming skills and a deep respect and love for farm animals.

Norwegians are the second largest ethnic group in Wisconsin. The first Norwegian settlers came to Jefferson, Rock and Dane counties. The Koshkonong colony in southeastern Dane County was founded in 1838; the Lake Muskego settlement in Waukesha and Racine counties began in 1839. Other major Norwegian settlements soon appeared in Vernon and Trempealeau counties. Seventy percent of the Norwegians in the United States lived in Wisconsin by 1850.

The Norwegians are proud of their heritage and hold many festivals each year; major ones are in Stoughton, Westby and Madison. The Norwegians actively promote Norwegian crafts, such as rosemaling (a type of painting) and woodcarving. And Norwegian foods abound. Stop at a restaurant in Stoughton or Westby—other places too—and you'll find lefse (a flat potato bread), meatballs, pickled beets and rice

*A sampling of German foods*

# THE LANDSCAPE

pudding for dessert. Of course, there is a never-ending supply of steaming coffee.

During fall, many Norwegian Lutheran churches serve lutefisk suppers. Lutefisk is a cod fish that is dried—to the consistency of a pine board, some say. The traditional way to prepare lutefisk is to soften it in lye water over several days, then boil it in salty water. Stories about lutefisk, especially its smell, play a prominent role in Wisconsin-Norwegian folklore.

The Poles are the third-largest ethnic group in Wisconsin. They came relatively late to the state, but they came in large numbers. In the 1940s, half of the farm population in Portage County was Polish. Other major settlements were Stevens Point (where a Polish-language newspaper, the only one in the United States, continues to be published), northwestern Waushara County, around Pulaski in Brown County, and Princeton in Green Lake County. Large numbers of Poles also are found in Milwaukee, Berlin, Beaver Dam, La Crosse and Manitowoc.

The Poles took naturally to farming, especially to vegetable growing. Because they came late to the state, they often found themselves on poor, sandy soil, but they turned it into beautiful fields of potatoes, cucumbers and green beans. The farmers' market was popular in Polish communities. Some of these markets were called cattle fairs because you could purchase not only vegetables but animals—everything from a bull calf to a feeder pig. Cities such as Princeton and Stevens Point had village squares for these weekly sales. They still do.

The polka continues to be a popular dance in Polish communities. Many Polish Catholic churches sponsor summer polka dances, and a good polka band is a necessity for a Polish wedding.

Many other ethnic groups made their mark on Wisconsin, as well. After the potato famine of 1846, large numbers of Irish fled their country and found their way to Wisconsin. Major Irish settlements appeared in Brown County, near Manitowoc, and in Washington, Waukesha, Dodge and several other counties. After the 1850s, Irish families settled in Polk County, St. Croix County (especially Erin Prairie) and Pierce

Swiss architecture in New Glarus

# THE LANDSCAPE

County. The Irish believed strongly in the importance of education. Many Irish became priests, nuns, teachers and attorneys. Most were Catholic and strong supporters of their church.

The Danes came to Wisconsin in the 1840s. They first settled around Racine but were soon found in Brown, Dane, Waushara, Winnebago, Dodge, Adams, Oconto, Portage and Polk counties. The Danish system of cooperative management was widely adopted in Wisconsin, from cheese factories to grain mills, feed stores and hospitals, and was a major contribution to the state. At one time, Wisconsin had more cooperatives than any other state in the nation. Danish baking is also well-known. Try some of Racine's famous Danish kringle, a kind of coffee cake, or perhaps some apple cake topped with whipped cream.

In 1845, Swiss agents came to Green County and made entry for 1,200 acres of land. In August of that year, more than a hundred Swiss immigrants settled in the Sugar River Valley. (Swiss also settled in other parts of Wisconsin, including Sauk and Buffalo counties.) Today, New Glarus, Monticello and Monroe are still steeped in Swiss traditions. In New Glarus you can visit a museum that recounts early farm life, schooling and Swiss cheesemaking. You can also travel around the village and see many buildings featuring Swiss architecture.

The Swiss are probably best known for their skills in making Swiss and Limburger cheeses. The only operating Limburger cheese factory in the United States is in Green County. And some Swiss cheese is still made the old-fashioned way with huge copper kettles. What causes the holes in Swiss cheese? During the curing process, bacteria in the pressed cheese give off carbon dioxide gradually, causing bubbles that result in holes. These same bacteria also help produce the pleasant hazelnut flavor characteristic of Swiss cheese. Visit the Monroe Cheese Festival, held on even-numbered years in Monroe, to capture some of the spirit of Green County's Swiss cheesemaking traditions. Stop by the Historic Cheesemaking Center in Monroe for the story of Swiss cheesemaking.

Most of Wisconsin's Amish came from Indiana and Ohio. (The Amish have German-

Swiss roots that trace back to when William Penn invited Amish people to live among the Quakers.) The first Amish to arrive in Wisconsin came to Medford, in Taylor County, in the 1920s, taking up farming on former pine land. Today there are Amish communities in Columbia, Marquette, Green Lake, Sauk, Vernon, Monroe, Portage, Waushara, Eau Claire, Clark, Dodge, Rock, Green, Buffalo and, perhaps, additional counties.

In contrast to other ethnic settlers, whose farming techniques changed as technology improved, the Amish have changed little. They still rely on draft horses for field power. They have no electricity or telephones, and they depend on their one-room schools to educate their children. They live together in tightly knit communities, adhering strongly to their religious beliefs. While traveling in Amish communities in Wisconsin, you frequently come upon buggies pulled by trotting horses. The Amish also operate little community stores, bakeries and craft shops that are open to the public. Look for signs pointing out these shops when traveling in Amish country.

## Lumbering and Farming

Upon their arrival, settlers immediately began clearing the land. The sound of the pioneer's ax—felling trees and preparing logs for cabins—echoed across the valleys. The pungent smell of burning wood filled the air as huge piles of branches and tree trunks were burned so crops could be planted.

The plowman's whip snapped over the backs of the ox teams as they leaned into their yokes, struggling to pull the wooden-beamed breaking plows through the rich soils of southern Wisconsin. Settlers planted wheat on these newly cleared fields, ultimately thousands of acres. By 1849, a year after Wisconsin became a state, farmers were harvesting 4 million bushels of wheat annually. Seven years later, it was 28 million bushels.

By the early 1860s, Wisconsin was the second-largest wheat-growing state in the nation and a major milling center. Water-powered mills appeared on rivers and

# THE LANDSCAPE

*white pine trees*

streams, turning wheat kernels into flour. Many of these old mills can be seen today; look for a millpond and chances are good you'll spot an old mill near the dam.

While wheat was occupying settlers in southern Wisconsin, white pine was king of the North Woods. At the time of settlement, immense pine lands lay in the region that roughly extends north of a line running from Manitowoc through Waupaca and Stevens Point and west to Chippewa Falls and St. Croix Falls. This vast forested area included nearly three-fifths of the state and, to many, seemed to be a limitless resource. Some commercial logging had begun by the 1840s, and, by the Civil War, Wisconsin's pine forests were providing thousands of board feet of building materials.

A soft and straight-grained wood, white pine lent itself well to building, and, because it was less dense than hardwood, it would float down the rivers. Pine logs could be moved from forest to saw mill via one of the state's many waterways. Just as flour mills sprung up in response to immense wheat crops, so did sawmills appear on every major river. By 1852, Oshkosh had become a major lumber town; it also milled tons of wheat flour. Same for La Crosse, which became a major lumber and flour-milling center in the western part of the state. There are still many operating sawmills in northern Wisconsin. To spot one, look for a pile of logs. The railroad slowly moved into the north in the

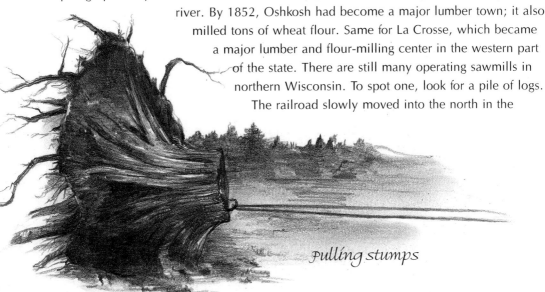

*pulling stumps*

# THE LANDSCAPE

1890s, and it became easier to transport logs by rail than by river. By shortly after the turn of the century, thousands upon thousands of acres of former pine forest lay naked. This area became known as the "cutover." Some of it was turned into farmland, but in much of the north the land was too thin for farming. In any case, the landscape was forever changed.

The more fertile land now grows alfalfa and corn. Holstein cows graze where pine trees once grew 80 feet tall. Today, there are thousands of acres of second-growth timber consisting of maple, aspen and evergreens such as balsam and spruce—much of it large enough to support the state's current lumber industry.

Wisconsin's lumbering era created millionaires and left behind wonderful stories of life in the woods—the lumber camps, the camp cooks, the bedbugs and the yell "daylight in the swamp," the cry that greeted the lumbermen each morning.

Meanwhile, in the southern part of the state, farming continued to be a major enterprise, one that was greatly transformed during the second half of the 19th century, as farmers shifted from the production of wheat to the production of milk.

Wheat growing had proved to be hard and tedious work. Seeds were planted by hand and cut with a cradle (a modified scythe). One man might cut three acres of wheat a day. The wheat was threshed by having oxen or horses walk over the grain to separate the kernels from the straw, or by hand with a flail, a long wooden handle to which a beater was attached with a leather throng. The flail threshing method was especially slow work.

Although the mechanical reaper was invented in 1835 by Cyrus McCormick, it was not used extensively until the Civil War (1861-1865), when there was a labor shortage. A refinement for the reaper, a knotter that tied the cut grain into bundles, was invented by John F. Appelby, who experimented in Mazomanie and then in Beloit in 1858. In 1837, J. I. Case of Racine designed and built a threshing machine that separated the grain kernels from their stalks and collected the grain. By the Civil War, Case was one of the largest manufacturers of farm machinery in the central United States. The grain drill, which allowed for mechanical planting of grain, was invented in 1841.

With these three inventions, wheat growing and harvesting became much easier, and, as time went on, more acres were planted. Then serious problems developed. Yields decreased because the same crop was grown year after year on the same ground with no fertilization. Disease, especially rust, began taking a toll. And a pesky little insect called the chinch bug overtook the wheat fields and literally sucked the juices from the plant.

By the 1870s, Wisconsin farmers were searching for alternative ways of making a living on the land. A brief spurt came from hops (used in beer making), which became an important crop about 1860. Hop growing made sense because Wisconsin had become a major brewing center by this time, a reputation it holds to this day. But with the hops market collapse in 1867, hops growing faded, never to return. In the 1850s, several farmers near Edgerton began growing tobacco, as did Norwegian farmers near Viroqua in Vernon County. In the central counties of the state, many farmers began growing potatoes. But none of these alternative crops could replace wheat in total economic value.

*Mill and millpond*

New Yorkers, who had come early to Wisconsin and were on the forefront of wheat growing, also knew dairy farming, which they had practiced in their home state. With wheat in decline, men like Hiram Smith began talking up the virtues of dairying and suggested that it might find a place in Wisconsin agriculture. In 1860, William Dempster Hoard of Fort

# THE LANDSCAPE

Atkinson founded a weekly newspaper, the *Jefferson County Union*, in which he began writing about the virtues of dairy cows. In 1885, he founded *Hoard's Dairyman* as a way of further promoting the emerging dairy industry. It is now a national magazine.

By 1900 Wisconsin had become a dairy state. Once-wilting wheat fields now grew pasture and hay crops for milk cows. Huge dairy barns began appearing throughout the state, and cheese and butter factories began springing up at the crossroads. Silos were built alongside the big barns, initially of fieldstones, then of wood, and later of concrete or metal. Wisconsin soon had more silos than any other state in the nation; one writer wrote that Wisconsin had twice as many silos as any other state. They were first built to store cut corn that fermented to make a nutritious and tasty cattle feed. Later, it was discovered that alfalfa made good silage, too. Today's silos include both corn silage and what is commonly called "haylage," which is silage made from hay.

The University of Wisconsin in Madison hired its first professor of agriculture, W. A. Henry, in 1880. Shortly after, the university was experimenting with silos, the feeding and management of dairy cows, and the control of various dairy cattle diseases. Steven Babcock, in 1890, invented the Babcock butterfat test, which provided a basis for milk payments received by farmers.

The number of dairy farms and dairy cows increased each year for many years. In 1867 there were 245,000 dairy cows in Wisconsin. In 1912 there were 1,460,000. In 1945 there were 2,585,000. These days, numbers are dropping. In 1996, there were about 1.5 million dairy cows in the state.

## Farming Today

During the past few decades, Wisconsin agriculture has gone through wrenching change. Although once the dairy farm and the family farm were synonymous, no longer is this always true. Family farms, with labor provided by the farm family, are disappearing. In 1960, Wisconsin boasted 138,000 farms, of which 105,000 were dairy farms. By 1994, Wisconsin had but 78,000 farms, with only 29,000 dairy farms. The average farm size increased from 161 acres in 1960 to 217 acres in 1994. And the average number of dairy cows per farm increased from 21 to 52, with many farmers milking more than a hundred cows, and some milking more than a thousand.

Thousands of farmers have left the land and moved to the city to seek alternative employment, or have sold their cows and begun working off the farm. Just as there was dramatic agricultural change in the late 1880s, when dairy farming replaced wheat growing, profound changes are occurring again, one hundred years later. Wisconsin has the largest number of dairy cows of any state and makes more cheese than any other, but its claim to producing the most milk was stolen away by California a few years ago.

Wisconsin has become a major vegetable producing state and a leading cranberry grower. Its forestry products still rank high as an economic resource, and Wisconsin makes more paper than any other state. But will the dairy cow eventually lose her throne? Will dairy farming become a specialized activity for a few huge operators, with hired hands doing the milking?

Traveling around Wisconsin, we see abandoned farms, visual reminders of the changes taking place in agriculture. Many of the proud old dairy barns stand empty, their fate unknown. What will Wisconsin's countryside look like a decade or two from now? Our landscape—the rolling hills, clear blue skies, lakes, streams and miles upon miles of protected northern forest land—will be as they are today. The face of agriculture is what will change. Fading from our view will be the small herds of dairy cows, grazing in pastures behind big red barns, waiting to be milked by a farmer and his family.

The
Farmstead

# THE FARMSTEAD

Farmsteads are the farm buildings at the center of a farming enterprise. Here is where the cattle are housed, the chickens kept, the hogs raised, and the field crops stored. Here, too, children are nurtured and friends are entertained.

Farms are food and fiber factories. But unlike most factory owners, farmers live on the premises. Thus, their leisure and work life are woven together, and it is often difficult to see where one stops and the other begins. Inspecting the fences, for example, although a worklike chore, is also a pleasurable activity for a father and his children. As they look for loose wires, they inspect the bluebird houses, listen for the meadow larks, and watch gophers scamper into rock piles. Because of this unique situation, farmsteads are more than a collection of buildings. They are symbols of a way of life.

## Placement of Farmstead Buildings

The placement of farm buildings is pleasing to the eye, especially when we find a farmstead at the end of a long valley, against the side of a hill, on top of a ridge or tucked up against a woodlot. Farmers, like most of us, are interested in beauty. But they don't locate their farm buildings with beauty as a first principle.

Farmsteads are arranged for ease in doing chores. The chicken house is close to the farmhouse. The corncrib is near the hog house. Prevailing winds are usually considered, too. No one wants to live in a house that is downwind from the pigpen.

In some instances, the layout of the farmstead has ethnic roots. Some of the early German farmsteads, for example, are arranged around a square courtyard.

Whether square or not, all farmsteads have a courtyard, also called a door-yard. The door-yard connects the farmstead to the road that passes by. Usually the barn anchors one side of the door-yard, and the farmhouse the other side. In between are the other outbuildings.

The door-yard is a gathering place, especially in summer when neighbors come by to share a tale about the weather, a problem they are having with a crop or the general price of farm goods, which is never high enough, it seems.

The farm dog is in charge of the door-yard. She greets all visitors with a friendly bark or two, keeps the chickens in the chicken yard, and watches over the children who are too young for farm work. The visiting salesman, the area politician and the pastor or priest are all greeted by the farm dog, with wagging tail and a bark or two to announce their arrival.

## Barns

The barn is usually the largest building on the farmstead. The majority of Wisconsin's wooden barns are bank barns, which are located next to a hill or manmade earthen bank—thus the name. Bank barns are two-story structures. The upper level, the hay mow, is designed to store hay. The lower level houses dairy cattle. Having the barn located next to an earthen bank enables the farmer to easily drive a load of hay into the upper floor of the barn for unloading.

Farmers like to capture as much sunlight as possible in the lower levels of the barn. And because the lower-level doors lead to the barnyard where the cattle exercise, the farmer wants this area protected from the frigid northwest winds that visit Wisconsin regularly during the long winter months. However, sometimes it was difficult to locate a barn next to a natural hillside and at the same time situate the barn so the doors and windows faced either to the south or to the east. Thus, many bank barns were built with ramps leading to the hay mows.

The earliest barns built in Wisconsin were constructed of logs. It is not difficult to find log barns, especially in Kewaunee and Door counties. Some beautiful examples of log barns also are found on Madeline Island, in Lake Superior off of Bayfield.

Gable-roofed wooden barns are the oldest frame barns found in Wisconsin. Some gable-roofed barns trace back to the early 1840s, before Wisconsin became a state. The oldest gable barns are known as "three-bay threshing" barns, and many were built when Wisconsin was a major wheat-growing state. These are one story tall and were designed as places where wheat could be threshed and stored. They did not house

# THE FARMSTEAD

cattle or horses. The three bays refer to the three sections of the barn: a threshing floor in the center and storage bays on each side. Large doors allowed the farmer to drive a load of wheat onto the threshing floor. Grain was usually threshed here by walking a horse or ox over the cut grain or sometimes by pounding the grain stalks with a flail (a stick with a leather thong to which a shorter stick was attached). After the threshing machine became popular in the late 1800s, the barn's threshing floor was no longer used for that purpose, although people often continued to call the middle bay by that name.

Many of the old gable-roofed barns were modified to house dairy cattle when dairy farming became popular in the late 1800s. Some were lifted off the ground and basement walls placed under them, thus making them two-story barns. Cattle were housed on the first story and hay was stored above. Other gable-roofed barns were modifed so that one bay housed cattle; the threshing floor and the other bay were left intact.

Gambrel-roofed barns were built between the late 1800s and the 1940s. Picture the back leg of a horse where the knee bends before the leg goes to the hoof. This part of the horse's anatomy (and that of other animals, too) is called the gambrel, and that is how this barn roof style got its name. The big dairy barns found throughout Wisconsin generally have gambrel roofs. Farmers built gambrel-roofed barns because they provide a large amount of space for storing hay. Some gambrel-roofed barns are bank barns, but many are not.

Once the hay fork was invented in 1867 and slowly became popular with farmers, it was no longer necessary to build barns with threshing floors for unloading hay. The hay fork is a device consisting of a series of ropes and pulleys with a metal harpoon (about 4 feet long with two prongs) that is thrust into a load of loose hay. The hay is lifted to the peak of the barn where a track transports the hay to the hay mow.

Using a hay fork, the farmer could drive to the outside end of the barn and lift the hay through an open door located near the peak of the roof. Many gambrel-roofed barns have an overhang thrusting out from the roof. This accommodates the hay fork track.

Barns with arch roofs were built in the 1940s and 1950s. They usually have two stories so that hay can be stored in the upper region and cattle housed below; most are not bank barns. By the time arch barns were built, farmers were using hay balers and elevators to transport hay bales into the hay storage area.

One-story steel barns came next. Many were constructed during the past 20 years, and many are being constructed today. They are sometimes found next to an older wooden barn but usually stand alone in newer farmsteads.

The most modern barn seen today in Wisconsin farmsteads is a plastic-covered greenhouse, similar to what you see at a garden center. They are relatively easy to erect and as easy to take down if the farmer wants to change direction in his operations. Another version of a greenhouse barn is one covered with canvas rather than plastic. The canvas covering, although still rather temporary when compared to a classic dairy barn, is nonetheless a bit more permanent than those covered with plastic. These experimental barns are not widely used, but are on the increase in Wisconsin farmsteads.

All barns so far mentioned are rectangular, and that is the most common barn shape. But several round barns are found in the state, as well as, more rarely, octagonal barns and others with more than eight sides. Vernon County, in western Wisconsin, claims to have the largest number of round barns of any county in the nation. Columbia County boasts a barn with 20 sides.

## Other Farm Buildings

The tallest and most visible structure in most farmsteads is the silo. It stores green cut corn that is allowed to ferment for later feeding to cattle. Farmsteads often include several silos: older, shorter ones and newer, taller ones.

Wisconsin has more silos than any other state, a reflection of the importance of silage as cattle feed. Compared to barns and even some of the other farmstead buildings, silos are relative newcomers. Wisconsin's first silo was built near Fort Atkinson in 1877. It was a trench 6 feet wide, 6 feet deep and 30 feet long—nothing at

# THE FARMSTEAD

all like today's concrete or blue-steel towers. It was several years before silos were built more above ground than below. The earliest above-ground structures were square and made of fieldstone. The next generation of silos were made of wood. The first of these wooden silos were square; later ones were octagonal and, finally, cylindrical. Recently, there has been a return to trench silos, not unlike the very first silo. The most modern silos resemble giant white plastic worms and lie out back of the barn, bulging with silage.

In addition to barns and silos, most farmsteads also include chicken houses, even if the farmer no longer raises chickens. The classic chicken house faces south or east and has a bevy of windows that allowed in as much sunlight as possible during the long winters when the chickens were confined. Chicken houses are usually rectangular in shape, one story tall, 14 feet or so wide and maybe 20-plus feet long.

Every farm once had a granary and a corncrib. Depending on what was grown on the farm, oats, rye or wheat were stored in the granary. The older wooden granaries are rather nondescript buildings, sometimes two stories tall, but often only one story with a gable roof. Early corncribs, still found in many farmsteads, were built narrow at the bottom and wider at the top, with ample space between the boards to promote drying of the cob corn. Today's granaries and corncribs are shiny, round steel buildings, and the grain is dried mechanically.

Depending on the kind of agriculture practiced, a farmstead may include a tobacco shed, potato cellar, pig house, beef barn or sheep shelter. Machine sheds for sheltering tractors and other expensive machinery are found in every farmstead.

## The Farmhouse

Without question, the barn is the most important building in the farmstead, more important even than the farmhouse. When repairs are needed on the barn, fixing the house usually waits. When a major addition is needed for the barn, house improvements are put off. It's a matter of priorities. After all, on a dairy farm it's the barn and what goes on inside it that provides income for the farm.

Farmhouses vary greatly. Many are wood frame, two stories tall, with a one-story ell that is the kitchen. Some are brick; a few are made of quarried rock.

The kitchen is the heart of the farmhouse; it has always been so. Farm kitchens are large enough to seat the entire family easily around the kitchen table. This is where the family gathers three times a day, nearly every day of the year. Kitchens are places for sharing and caring, for dreaming of tomorrow and telling stories about yesterday. Here is where farmers, their families and their neighbors gather. Exceptions are holidays and when company comes; then the dining room is used.

In the old farmhouses, the least-used room was the living room, or parlor, as it was sometimes called. It was saved for the most special of times, when a city relative came to visit or for a wedding or funeral. Otherwise, it was unused—a kind of shrine. Not too many years ago, many farmers closed off the parlor to save heat. Why heat a room that was never used?

Hallways and vestibules and other fancy attributes are often missing from old farmhomes. Walk through the kitchen door and you are in the kitchen. No deciding which way to turn; through the door and you are in. And the door from one room leads to another room: kitchen to dining room, dining room to living room, living room to bedroom. No hallways to take up space.

All in all, farmsteads are special places in the countryside. They generally feature a barn and are punctuated with one or more silos, but they are much more than collections of farm buildings. They serve a practical purpose, yet are artistically pleasing. They represent agricultural history, yet they tell the story of farming today. They are business centers, yet they reflect a way of life.

# FARMSTEAD DESIGN

*A farmstead is* a grouping of farm buildings, including the farmhouse. Barns are the largest buildings on dairy farms, 40 or more feet wide and as much as 150 feet long. Silos are the tallest structures—some stretch upward of 100 feet and may be 30 feet in diameter.

Farmsteads are visual reminders of a farm's history. Old and new buildings stand next to each other, the older ones often converted to modern-day uses. A former woodshed may be a workshop; a carriage shed might be a garage. The farmstead depicted here contains buildings tracing back to the 1800s. That means it has been a working farm for several generations.

# BARN STYLES

The storage area for hay is called the hay mow (rhymes with "cow").

Bank barn

cattle are housed in the basement of a bank barn.

# Three-bay threshing barn

*Of the three* main barn styles found in Wisconsin, the bank barn is the most common. Designed for dairy cows, it was built next to a bank or with a ramp leading up to the floor where hay was stored. Cows were housed in the basement. The three-bay threshing barn, built during Wisconsin's wheat-growing era, was divided into three sections in which wheat could be threshed and stored. The barn designed for a hay fork contains ropes and pulleys that lift hay from outside the barn into the hay mow.

## Barn designed for a hay fork

# BARN ROOFS

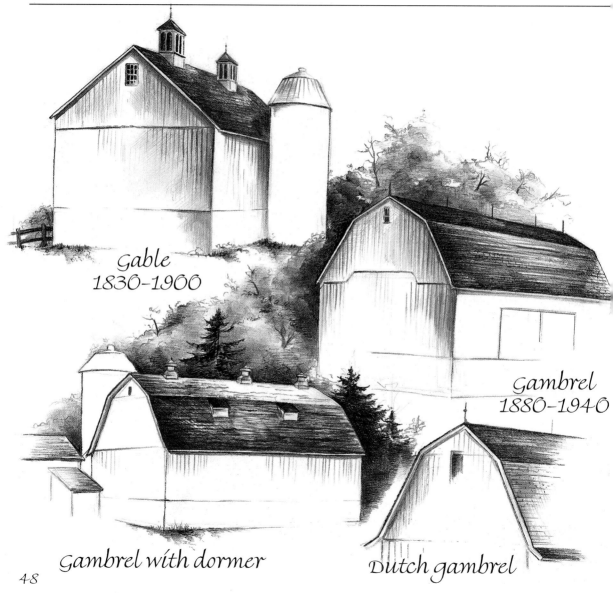

Gable
1830–1900

Gambrel
1880–1940

Gambrel with dormer

Dutch gambrel

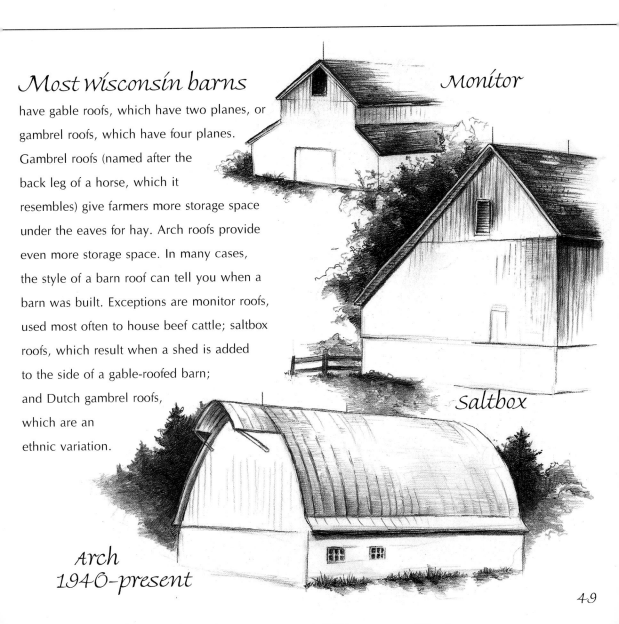

## Most Wisconsin barns

have gable roofs, which have two planes, or gambrel roofs, which have four planes. Gambrel roofs (named after the back leg of a horse, which it resembles) give farmers more storage space under the eaves for hay. Arch roofs provide even more storage space. In many cases, the style of a barn roof can tell you when a barn was built. Exceptions are monitor roofs, used most often to house beef cattle; saltbox roofs, which result when a shed is added to the side of a gable-roofed barn; and Dutch gambrel roofs, which are an ethnic variation.

*Monitor*

*Saltbox*

*Arch
1940-present*

# CENTRIC BARNS

Labels within the interior diagram:

MANURE ALLEY
COW STALLS
MANGER
FEED ALLEY
MANGER
COW STALLS
MANURE ALLEY
SILO
FEED ROOM
BULL PEN
CALVES
CALVES
STALLS

*Round barn interior*

*Round barn*

octagonal barn

**Round barns** became fashionable
in the late 1800s after it was discovered that they could be
built with the same amount of material as a conventional barn
yet provide more space. When barn builders found it was difficult to
curve wood, they began to build octagonal barns with eight flat sides.
These were promoted by a popular speaker of the day, Orson Fowler, who believed
the human brain was divided into eight parts and that eight-sided structures must thus be
a natural form. These "centric" barns did not become widespread, however, because most
farmers thought a circular building was out of place on square farm property.

51

# ETHNIC BARNS

By 1900, more than 50 ethnic groups had settled in Wisconsin. They employed various building styles, which changed over time. Here are a few examples.

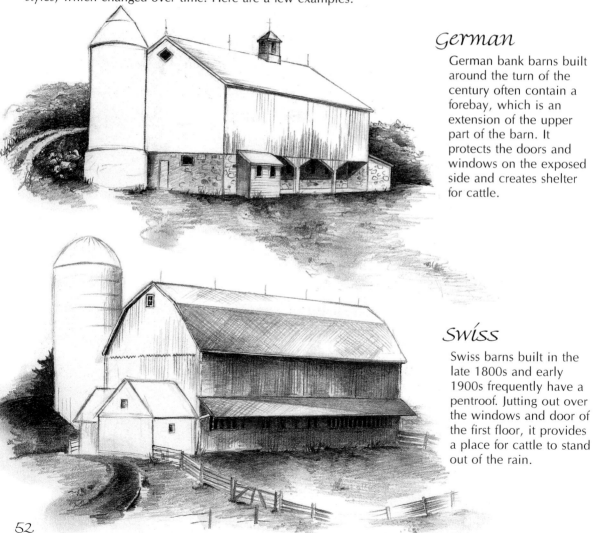

## German

German bank barns built around the turn of the century often contain a forebay, which is an extension of the upper part of the barn. It protects the doors and windows on the exposed side and creates shelter for cattle.

## Swiss

Swiss barns built in the late 1800s and early 1900s frequently have a pentroof. Jutting out over the windows and door of the first floor, it provides a place for cattle to stand out of the rain.

## Finnish

In the 1890s, Finns, who were meticulous builders, used logs hewed on all four sides and fit them tightly together. Several of these barns were built in Douglas County.

## Swedish

In contrast to the Finns, the Swedes hewed their logs on the top and bottom only and were less concerned about fitting them tightly together.

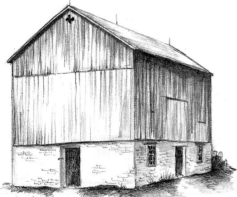

## Welsh

A typical 1840 Welsh barn had two stories, a fieldstone or quarried rock wall and a gable roof. Welsh barns can be found in Waukesha County and in Columbia County.

## Amish

You can identify an Amish barn by the absence of electrical lines and, often, by the presence of draft horses.

# BUILDING MATERIALS

The materials with which a barn was built reflect the era, and sometimes the region, in which it was constructed. Farmers have always favored practicality.

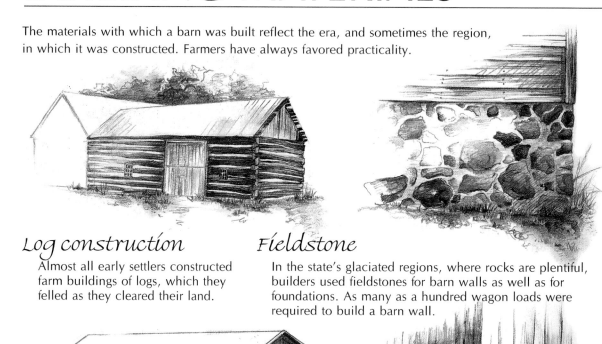

## Log construction

Almost all early settlers constructed farm buildings of logs, which they felled as they cleared their land.

## Fieldstone

In the state's glaciated regions, where rocks are plentiful, builders used fieldstones for barn walls as well as for foundations. As many as a hundred wagon loads were required to build a barn wall.

## Quarried rock

Quarried rock, taken from bedrock, is frequently found in barns in the unglaciated southwest. Building with rock and stone requires advanced masonry skills.

# Stovewood construction

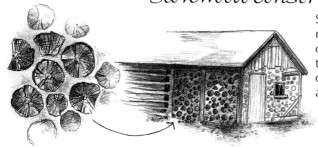

Stovewood can be seen in barns in the northeast, where cedar and tamarack once were plentiful. Stovewood is easier to build with than fieldstone and was often used by farmers who couldn't afford to hire a stonemason.

# Modern two-story steel barn

# Greenhouse barn

Barns constructed of plastic with aluminum frames are inexpensive and represent the latest trend in barn construction.

# Modern one-story steel barn

Steel barns are partially prefabricated for ease in construction and are long-lasting.

# BARN DECORATIONS

Even plain barns are beautiful, with pleasing lines and cathedral-like spaces. Still, farmers sometimes add decorative elements. Adornments may have a practical use or may be "just for pretty."

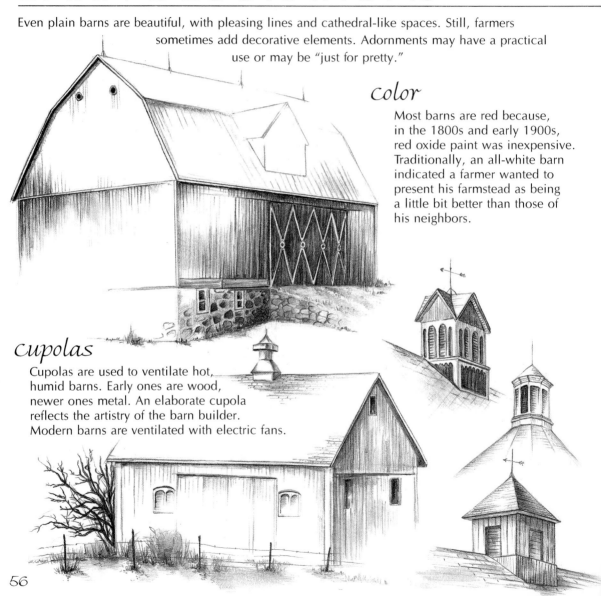

## color

Most barns are red because, in the 1800s and early 1900s, red oxide paint was inexpensive. Traditionally, an all-white barn indicated a farmer wanted to present his farmstead as being a little bit better than those of his neighbors.

## cupolas

Cupolas are used to ventilate hot, humid barns. Early ones are wood, newer ones metal. An elaborate cupola reflects the artistry of the barn builder. Modern barns are ventilated with electric fans.

## Lightning rods & weather vanes

A shattered ball on a lightning rod means the barn has been struck by lightning (or by a shot from the neighbor kid's .22 rifle). Weather vanes help farmers predict the next day's weather so they can plan their work—or other activities. An old saying:

*"Wind in the west, fish bite best."*

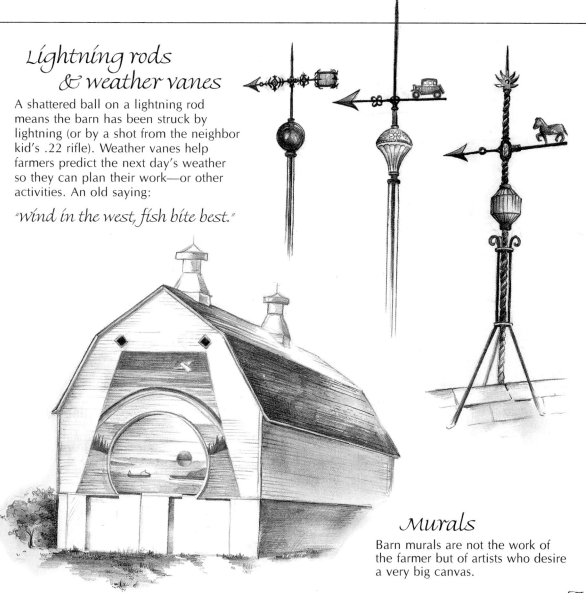

## Murals

Barn murals are not the work of the farmer but of artists who desire a very big canvas.

# SILOS

## Wisconsin contains

more silos and more kinds of
silos than any other state. Farmers
blow chopped corn or hay into
a silo, where it is allowed to
naturally ferment for a month
or so. This "silage," moist and
with a slightly acidic taste, is
fed to livestock, who relish it.
To date a silo, note the material
with which it was made.

*1880s*
*Square fieldstone silo*

*Late 1800s*
*Multi-sided wooden silo*

*Early 1900s*
*Brick silo*

*Early 1900s–1990s*
*Poured concrete silo*

*Early 1900s–1990s*
*cement stave silo*

**1880s**
*Cylindrical fieldstone silo*

**Turn of the century**
*Wood stave silo*

**Early 1900s**
*Hollow tile silo*

**Late 1940s-1990s**
*Blue glass-lined silo*

**1980s-1990s**
*Concrete-sided bunker silo*

**1990s**
*Plastic tube silo*

# FARMHOUSE STYLES

*As with barns,* the architectural style of a farmhouse reflects the era in which it was constructed. The L-shaped farmhouse was built after the Civil War and into the early 1900s. It combined a gable-roofed two-story section with a wing that was either one or two stories. A one-story porch was common.

*The square farmhouse*, with four equal-sized rooms on each floor, a hipped roof and large front porch, is referred to as the American Foursquare. Economical and practical, it was popular from about 1900 to 1940. Wood, brick and stone have all been used to build houses. Cornish and Welsh masons were particularly skilled with limestone quarried from deposits that underlie much of the state.

# OTHER FARMSTEAD BUILDINGS

The other structures on a farmstead will tell you what activities the farm family is currently engaged in or what it may have undertaken in the past.

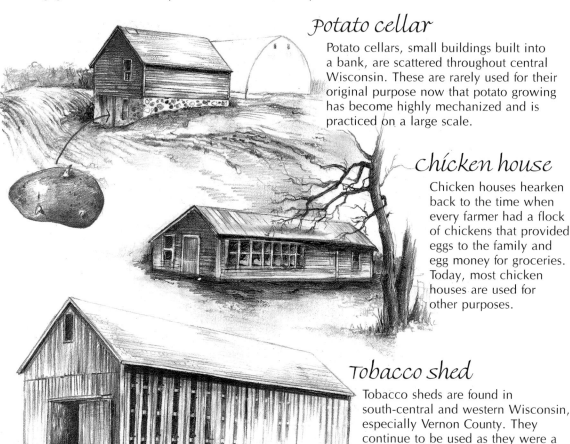

### Potato cellar

Potato cellars, small buildings built into a bank, are scattered throughout central Wisconsin. These are rarely used for their original purpose now that potato growing has become highly mechanized and is practiced on a large scale.

### chicken house

Chicken houses hearken back to the time when every farmer had a flock of chickens that provided eggs to the family and egg money for groceries. Today, most chicken houses are used for other purposes.

### Tobacco shed

Tobacco sheds are found in south-central and western Wisconsin, especially Vernon County. They continue to be used as they were a century ago. Hinged doors on both sidewalls open so that tobacco hanging inside will air-dry.

## corncrib

Corncribs allow for natural drying of the corn crop.

## calf hutch

Dairy calves are housed in individual calf hutches, which are comfortable, healthy structures for a growing animal.

## windmill

Windmills once pumped water on many Wisconsin farms, especially before the arrival of electricity.

## steel granaries

These round steel structures replaced wooden granaries and corn cribs. They hold thousands of bushels. Propane heaters with blowers dry the corn.

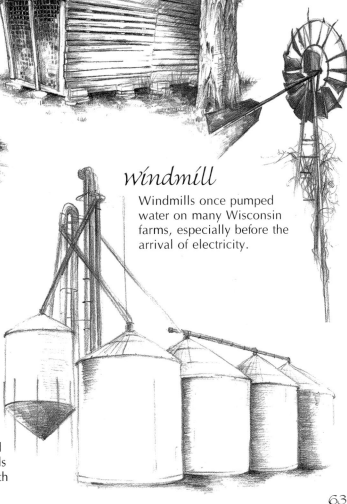

Crops

# CROPS

Many believe that Wisconsin's agriculture begins and ends with the dairy cow. Not so. Dairy cows are extremely important—after all, this is the "dairy state." But Wisconsin is also a major producer of crops. And while some crops, such as alfalfa and corn, are grown to feed the ever-hungry dairy cow, Wisconsin is a national leader in the production of several vegetable and fruit crops, which are processed here and shipped throughout the country.

Wisconsin lends itself well to crop production. There is ample rainfall (on average more than 30 inches per year), a growing season that exceeds 100 days in much of the state, and soil that is fertile and generally easy to work. Underground water sources are ample and within easy reach of modern-day irrigation pumps. The long, sometimes harsh winters actually can benefit crop growing; below-zero temperatures destroy or help control many insect pests.

Unfortunately, a can of peas or sweet corn does not have as much appeal as a Holstein cow grazing in an alfalfa field. But a case can be made that Wisconsin is a crop state. Here is information about the most common crops you'll see as you travel around.

## Forage Crops

The term "forage" comes from "foraging" and a time when cattle had to search for what they ate. The most common forage crop in the state is alfalfa. When you see dairy cows on pasture, that's what they are probably eating—an 18-inch-tall, dense-growing, small-leafed plant with blue flowers. Some farmers cut fresh alfalfa every day and haul it to a feedlot for their cattle.

Alfalfa becomes hay after it is allowed to dry and is baled into square or round bales. Almost every farmer makes hay from alfalfa. Alfalfa is also used for silage. Silage is made by cutting the crop, allowing it to partially dry, and then blowing it into a silo where it ferments. Alfalfa, whether in the form of hay or silage, will keep throughout the winter and provide a ready source of feed.

Other common forage crops are red and sweet clover. Red clover has a pinkish-red blossom; sweet clover is a tall, rank plant with a yellow flower. All forage crops have a pleasant smell when drying, and sweet clover has the sweetest smell of all. The best time to capture the full aroma of drying hay is on a warm, humid night in June, when a haze hangs in the valley and the spring breeze has gone to bed with the sun.

Grasses found in Wisconsin's pastures and hayfields are also forage crops. Commonly grown forage grasses are brome grass and timothy, with the latter less common today than several years ago. Generally, the grasses are mixed with alfalfa and clover, so they are harder to spot.

## Corn

Wisconsin's most popular grain crops are corn, oats, soybeans, wheat and rye. Wisconsin farmers grow about four million acres of corn, making the state eighth in the nation in corn grain production. Much of the corn grain is used for feeding dairy cattle, beef cattle and pigs. Some of it is sold off the farm where it is used for everything from cornflakes to ethanol fuel.

Corn is planted from late April to mid-May, in rows up to 30 inches apart. New corn plants look like large spears of grass as they emerge from the soil. By early June, corn plants are usually only a few inches above the ground. A time-honored goal for Wisconsin farmers is to have their corn at least "knee-high by the Fourth of July." Before the end of July it is shoulder-high or taller. By midsummer, corn plants begin "tasseling." The corn tassel looks like a little tan tree stuck on top of each corn plant. When the tassels appear, the corn plant's ears are also developing on the side of the plant. It is on the ear, of course, that the corn cob and kernels are found. In September, corn plants are taller than the tallest person, often more than 7 feet tall. By October and first frost, corn plants begin drying and turning brown. With frost, the entire plant is killed, and the dead leaves rustle in the wind, the ears drying naturally in the autumn sun. An acre of corn yields up to 150 bushels, sometimes more, but often less.

Corn is not grown in far northern Wisconsin because there are too few frost-free

# CROPS

growing days. Corn requires upwards of 80 days to mature. The longer the growing season, the greater the yield.

Thousands of acres of field corn are made into silage and fed to dairy cattle. Silage corn requires fewer growing days than grain corn, and thus is adaptable to most of the state. Wisconsin leads the nation in the production of corn silage, producing an estimated 8.5 million tons of the fermented product. To make corn silage, the entire corn plant is chopped into small pieces with a forage cutter and then blown into a silo where it is allowed to ferment. During the fermentation process, a strong acid develops that prevents the growth of rotting organisms. The resulting product has a unique smell and appearance, not at all like the corn plant from which it came. Dairy cattle relish the slightly acid-tasting silage.

## Oats

Most of the oats grown in Wisconsin are fed to cows and horses. Oat straw, left after the grain is removed from the oat plant, is a popular bedding for dairy and other farm animals. Oats are also grown as a nurse crop for legumes such as alfalfa and clover. Oats and the legume crops are planted together. The tiny legume plants are shaded by the oat plants and, because oats grow faster than most weeds, the legumes have less competition from weeds. By the time the oat crop is harvested in late summer, the legumes are well established and can grow on their own.

Oats are planted as early as farmers can work their fields in the spring. A week or so after planting, the oat plants emerge and the field turns from brown to green. Unlike corn, which is planted in rows far enough apart so that weed-control equipment can pass through, oats are planted in rows only a few inches apart. A new oat field looks like a giant lawn.

Soon the oats are knee high, and then the oat seeds begin emerging. The oat seed develops on top of the oat plant—a process called "heading." By early July, oats are headed, and by late July the oat plants turn from green to gold, as the plant matures and the oat seeds ripen. By late July and early August, combines move through the oat fields, harvesting the oat seeds.

## Soybeans

Wisconsin grows about 900,000 acres of soybeans, primarily in the southern part of the state. Soybeans are grown as a cash crop, which means they are sold off the farm. The soybean plant, which has hairy stems and seed pods resembling green beans, grows about 2 feet tall. The seeds are usually planted in early May, and the crop is harvested in fall when the deep-green plants dry and turn brown.

Few farm crops are used more widely than soybeans. Printer's ink is made from soybeans, so is plastic and, of course, tofu. Imitation hamburger is a soybean product. Soybean oil is used in paints, varnishes, linoleum and soap. A rich source of protein, soybeans are widely used as animal feed.

## Wheat, Rye and Barley

In the 1860s, Wisconsin was the second-largest producer of wheat in the nation, but because of disease and insect problems, wheat almost disappeared from the state. Today, Wisconsin farmers rank 33rd in wheat production, growing about 145,000 acres of winter wheat and about 10,000 acres of spring wheat. Winter wheat is planted in the fall and harvested the following summer. Spring wheat is planted in the spring and harvested in late summer.

Rye is grown primarily in the central counties and does well on poor land. Rye often is planted in autumn on lighter soils to help prevent wind erosion during the winter months. While Wisconsin once grew considerable barley—the state's breweries were a ready market—today, barley is a minor crop.

## Vegetable Crops

Wisconsin produces more green beans and sweet corn than any other state—nearly

# CROPS

one-third of all the green beans and more than a fifth of the sweet corn grown for processing. It also grows more beets; about half of the country's beets come from Wisconsin. The state ranks among the top three in production of peas, cabbage for kraut, and cucumbers for pickles. Only three states, Idaho, Washington and North Dakota, grow more potatoes than Wisconsin. Wisconsin ranks fourth in the nation in the production of carrots.

Where do you look for these crops? With the exception of potatoes, which can be found as far north as Oneida and Langlade counties, vegetable crops are grown in the central counties—the so-called central sands region that includes Waushara, Portage, Marquette and Wood counties—and in southern counties such as Sauk, Columbia, Racine, Kenosha and Jefferson. You will find carrots, some lettuce for the fresh market, onions, sod, mint and cranberries growing on low land or muck soil areas of the state. Cabbage is grown in southern Wisconsin, but can also be found in the northeastern part of the state.

A clue for spotting potatoes, cucumbers, peas, green beans and sweet corn is to look for the huge irrigation sweeps that slowly move across the fields, spraying water on ever-thirsty crops. Irrigation has made vegetable growing profitable on the sandy soils of central Wisconsin. Without irrigation, a farmer might harvest 25 100-pound bags of potatoes per acre; with it, he can grow more than 10 times that amount.

## cranberries

Settlers in northern Green Lake and southern Waushara counties discovered wild cranberries growing in the marshes. By 1853, cranberries were grown commercially. Today, Wisconsin is the largest producer of cranberries in the country; Massachusetts is in second place.

Cranberries are grown in 18 of Wisconsin's 72 counties, with the majority of the 13,000 acres in Wood, Jackson and Monroe counties. The annual crop is valued at about $75 million, making it Wisconsin's most important fruit crop.

The Ocean Spray Cooperative represents about 80 percent of the cranberry acres grown in the state, and has receiving stations near Babcock and Tomah. The Ocean Spray receiving station at Tomah is the world's largest.

Manmade cranberry marshes appear as flat fields with dikes and water-filled ditches surrounding them. Cranberries grow through the summer, turn red in fall and are ready for picking in late September and October. In the early years of cranberry growing, cranberries were picked by hand with pickers working on their hands and knees. Later, cranberry marshes were flooded so that the red fruit floated to the surface. Cranberry rakes—large boxes with tines on one end—caught the berries and pulled them off the vines. Since about 1950, mechanical harvesters have been used to beat the berries off the vines. The red fruit is then floated to a conveyor belt and loaded onto trucks.

## Apples and Cherries

Apples came with the first white settlers in the 1830s and 1840s. Commercial apple orchards are found in 46 of Wisconsin's 72 counties, with most orchards clustered around Gays Mills and in Door and Bayfield counties. Because of the milder climate near Lake Michigan and Green Bay, cherries do well in Door County. Wisconsin is fifth among the states in cherry production.

May is apple- and cherry-blossom time, and a good time for visiting orchard country. Harvesting starts in July for cherries and continues on into the fall for apples—another good opportunity for an orchard visit. Many cherry and apple orchards have "pick-your-own" arrangements, an opportunity to experience the orchards firsthand.

## Mint and Sod

Ever wonder how spearmint gum, mint mouthwash, mint toothpaste and candy mints got their minty taste? The mint probably came from Wisconsin. Some 40,000 acres of mint are grown here, on muck soils.

When you drive near a mint field, especially if it is a warm, humid summer evening,

# CROPS

the mint smell will be in the air. A good place to look for mint is along Interstate 94 between Madison and Milwaukee. Other mint growing areas are near Montello, Pardeeville, Sun Prairie, Beaver Dam, Fort Atkinson and Whitewater.

While growing, mint looks somewhat like alfalfa, except it's taller. Growers harvest the crop by cutting it with a haybine—the same machine used for cutting alfalfa hay— and allowing the plants to wilt for one to two days. Using a forage harvester, the partially dried mint plants are then chopped into a metal mint tub mounted on a wagon. The chopped material is hauled to a machine that steams out the mint oil. The steam carries the mint oil to a condenser, where it is cooled. Finally, a separator drains off the mint oil. One acre can produce up to 50 pounds of oil.

Sod growers, usually located on muck soils, grow lawn grass, which is lifted off the surface of a field in 18-inch strips, rolled up and delivered to garden centers and landscapers for use in making new urban lawns. Sod growers are usually found near large cities; several are located between Milwaukee and Madison.

## Tobacco

When the first Europeans came to this country, they saw Indians smoking tobacco. By the 1600s, Virginia and Carolina farmers were growing and shipping tobacco to Europe. As the settlers moved west, they took tobacco seeds with them. In 1850, farmers near Edgerton, in southern Wisconsin, planted the first tobacco in the state. Wisconsin soon developed a reputation for growing fine cigar tobacco, and by 1900 some 50 tobacco warehouses operated in Edgerton. Farmers in the Viroqua-Westby area also discovered they could grow tobacco.

Since the early days, tobacco growing has been viewed as a "cash crop"—some extra money for a dairy farmer. Tobacco growers usually grow only two to six acres. (Government quotas limit the acres planted.) Tobacco growing is highly labor-intensive. The plants are hand-hoed and topped, the flowering stalk removed to assure higher-quality leaves. Harvesting, which begins in late August, involves hand cutting the leaves and piling and hanging them in a tobacco shed for drying.

# Ginseng

Traveling along Highway 51 in the Wausau area, you may see unusual-looking slatted structures on tall poles in many fields. Ginseng, one of Wisconsin's most exotic plants, grows beneath the slats. Wisconsin is the nation's leading ginseng producer.

Ginseng is native to North America and grows wild in many northern forests, including those in Wisconsin. In the early 1800s, it was discovered that ginseng could be cultivated—transplanted from the woods and grown in artificially shaded conditions.

Nearly all ginseng grown in the state is exported to Asia where it is used as an aphrodisiac and endurance builder. Many claim its use delays and prevents physical exhaustion. The name ginseng comes from the Chinese *jen-shen*, which means "man root." The ginseng root, the part that is harvested, dried and shipped, often resembles the human figure. If the two lower portions, or legs, are of equal length, the root is considered male. If of unequal length, they are female. The male root is considered more valuable.

Ginseng has several unique characteristics. The seeds take 18 months to germinate, and the plant is allowed to grow for six years before the roots are harvested. Each winter the plant dies back and starts growing again the following spring. Ginseng cannot be grown on the same plot of ground more than once; residues are left in the soil, preventing a new crop from growing. Sometimes a ginseng grower forgets where he may have had a bed several years ago. If a new ginseng bed overlaps an old bed, he can see exactly the location of the old bed because the new plants will not grow there.

If not harvested, ginseng has been known to live for more than a hundred years. There are presently about 1,500 ginseng growers in Wisconsin, and the number is increasing. In addition to those in Marathon County, a few growers in Vernon County are beginning to plant the crop.

# CROPS

## Sphagnum Moss

Sphagnum moss is sometimes called Wisconsin's invisible industry. Relatively few people realize the state is a major producer of this naturally grown product. Because sphagnum moss, when dry, can hold up to 20 times its weight in water, it is invaluable for shipping nursery plants. It has also been used for surgical dressings and for seed germination when there is danger of fungus attacking seeds.

Grown in natural marshes, often near cranberries, sphagnum moss replaces itself after harvesting. A crop can be harvested about every five years. To harvest, the moss is pulled, hauled from the marsh to high ground and dried. It is then baled and shipped throughout the world. Harvest season runs from spring through late fall.

## Lumber and Pulpwood

Wisconsin has a long history as a lumber state, going back to the late 1800s. Even today, trees for lumber are a major Wisconsin crop, both hardwoods for fine furniture and soft woods for framing and other uses.

Pulpwood, for paper, is another major forestry crop. For many years, Wisconsin has been the leading producer of paper in the United States. Traveling through the state's central and northern regions, you often can spot piles of small-diameter logs cut into 8-foot lengths. These have recently been cut and hauled out of the woods in preparation for trucking to the paper mills in central and northeastern Wisconsin. You'll often see pulp trucks in the area, semis in two sections with a loading machine attached to one section.

## Christmas Trees

Christmas trees are found mostly in Waushara County but also grow in other regions. Thousands of acres of Scotch pine, spruce and Frasier fir are planted in long rows that wind around the hillsides. In eight to 10 years, the trees are cut and shipped to cities throughout the country. About a thousand trees are planted per acre. After established, some species, such as Scotch pine, are sheared yearly to shape them and make them fuller. Many high school students, wielding machetes, spend their summers shearing Christmas trees.

In central Wisconsin in mid-April, you may see a tree planter working in an open field, the operator sitting in the back of the plowlike machine, thrusting tiny trees into the slit the machine makes in the soil. Later in the summer, you may see a huge space-age machine with long spiderlike legs working in the tree plantations. It's a sprayer used to control various insect pests that attack young trees. Another version of the machine sprays some of the trees green, making sure that they are a uniform color for the discriminating Christmas shopper. Late October through November, Christmas trees are cut, machine-wrapped in twine or plastic netting, and loaded onto trucks for shipment.

## Maple Syrup

In the spring, the state's maple syrup producers, located in a 150-mile band across the central part of the state from Langlade County in the east to Pierce County in the west, begin tapping maple trees for their sweet sap. Some 3,000 to 4,000 maple syrup producers tap anywhere from a few trees to several thousand during the first warm days of March. Wisconsin is the fourth-largest maple syrup state, producing about 10 percent of the country's maple syrup, or about 120,000 gallons annually. Vermont is the leader.

Native Americans taught the settlers how to tap maple trees and make syrup. The process is relatively simple. A hole is drilled in a sugar maple tree, a spigot is pushed into the hole, a bucket is attached, and the sap is allowed to collect. In the larger maple syrup operations, plastic tubing is used to collect the sap, saving considerable labor. The sap is then boiled in open kettles, flat pans or modern-day stainless-steel evaporators. Before boiling, sap has a sugar content of about two percent. Once boiled down to syrup, the sugar content increases to 65 percent. It takes about 40 gallons of maple sap to produce one gallon of syrup, so lots of boiling is necessary. Once the sap becomes golden-brown syrup, it is put in cans or bottles and is ready for sale.

# FORAGE CROPS

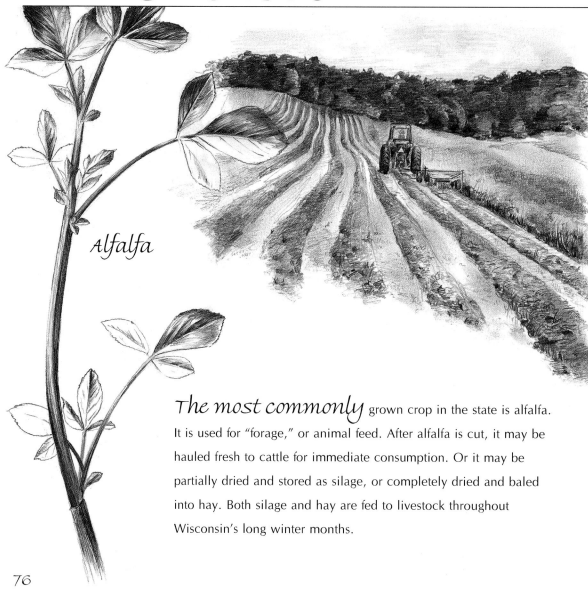

Alfalfa

*The most commonly* grown crop in the state is alfalfa. It is used for "forage," or animal feed. After alfalfa is cut, it may be hauled fresh to cattle for immediate consumption. Or it may be partially dried and stored as silage, or completely dried and baled into hay. Both silage and hay are fed to livestock throughout Wisconsin's long winter months.

*Red Clover* is not as popular as alfalfa, but it is sometimes planted with it. The mix is used for silage and hay. You can't miss the red clover blossom, reddish pink in color. Timothy is grown primarily as hay for horses. Its distinctive characteristic is its head, which is really a flower.

*Red clover*

*Timothy*

*Alfalfa*

# GRAIN CROPS

*In early May,* Wisconsin farmers plant about 4 million acres of corn, much of which is used for cattle feed. Given lots of sunshine, warm temperatures and ample rainfall, corn grows more rapidly than almost any other plant. The standard many farmers use is "knee high by the Fourth of July." By September, this amazing plant is 7 to 10 feet tall. You'll often see alfalfa and corn, both essential feed crops, growing side by side in farmers' fields. Much of Wisconsin's corn crop is made into corn silage, especially in the northern and central parts of the state. There, the growing season is only about 75 days long, and corn must be harvested in an immature stage, while it is still green. To harvest corn as grain, an 85- to 100-day growing season is required.

*corn*

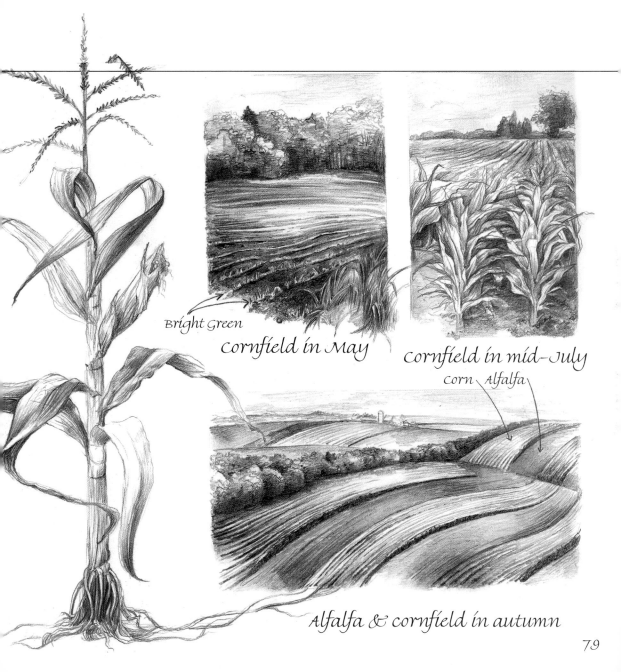

Bright Green

*cornfield in May*

*cornfield in mid-July*

corn   Alfalfa

*Alfalfa & cornfield in autumn*

# GRAIN CROPS

## Soybeans are grown

as a "cash crop," which means that farmers sell the soybean seeds. They are used for an incredible variety of products, including livestock feed, diesel fuel, plastics and artificial hamburgers. Soybeans grow best in southern Wisconsin, where there are heavier soils and a longer growing season. To distinguish a soybean plant from a green bean plant, which it resembles, look for hairy stems and fuzzy bean pods.

*Soybeans*

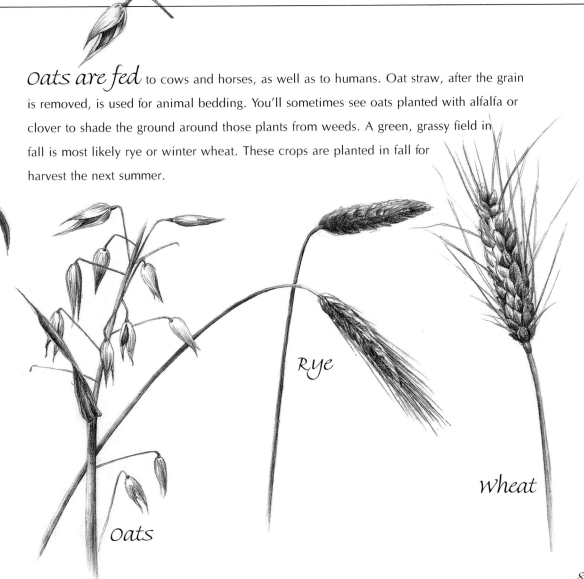

**Oats are fed** to cows and horses, as well as to humans. Oat straw, after the grain is removed, is used for animal bedding. You'll sometimes see oats planted with alfalfa or clover to shade the ground around those plants from weeds. A green, grassy field in fall is most likely rye or winter wheat. These crops are planted in fall for harvest the next summer.

Rye

Wheat

Oats

# VEGETABLES

## Green beans

Wisconsin leads the nation in the production of green beans. Most of the crop is grown in Waushara, Marquette, Portage, Wood and Adams counties.

## Peas

Peas are planted in early spring and harvested in June. Farmers will often plant green beans in the former pea field and harvest two crops in the same growing season.

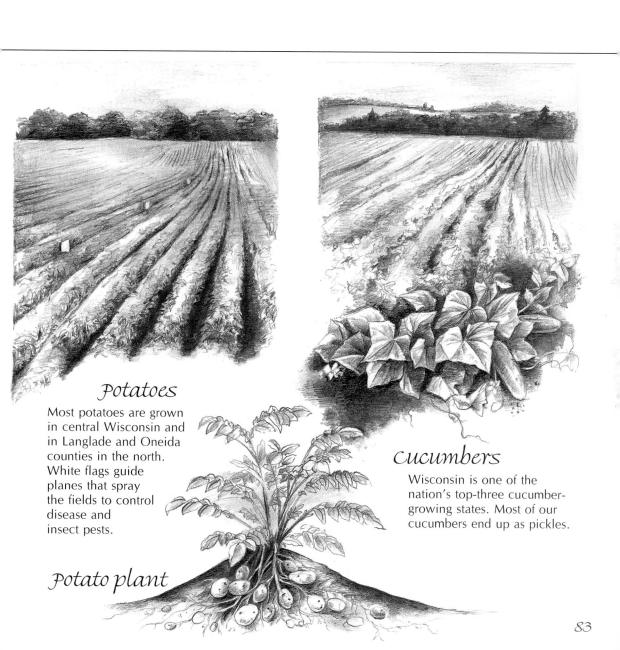

## Potatoes

Most potatoes are grown in central Wisconsin and in Langlade and Oneida counties in the north. White flags guide planes that spray the fields to control disease and insect pests.

## Cucumbers

Wisconsin is one of the nation's top-three cucumber-growing states. Most of our cucumbers end up as pickles.

## Potato plant

# VEGETABLES

*orange carrot stubs after harvesting*

## carrots

Wisconsin ranks fourth in the nation in the production of carrots. The crop is grown primarily in marshy areas in the southern and southeastern parts of the state. A harvesting machine digs the carrot out by the roots.

## cabbage

Cabbage is a major Wisconsin crop, with most of it used for sauerkraut.

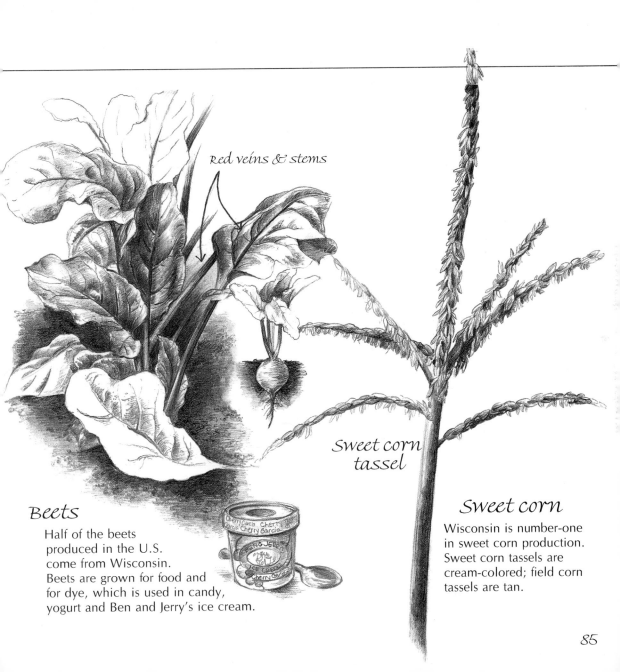

Red veins & stems

Sweet corn
tassel

## Beets

Half of the beets
produced in the U.S.
come from Wisconsin.
Beets are grown for food and
for dye, which is used in candy,
yogurt and Ben and Jerry's ice cream.

## Sweet corn

Wisconsin is number-one
in sweet corn production.
Sweet corn tassels are
cream-colored; field corn
tassels are tan.

85

# FRUIT

## cranberries

Wisconsin is the nation's number-one cranberry state. At harvest time, cranberry marshes are flooded. The hollow berries float to the surface and are shaken loose from the plant by machine. The "craneberry" takes its name from the sandhill crane, which it resembles.

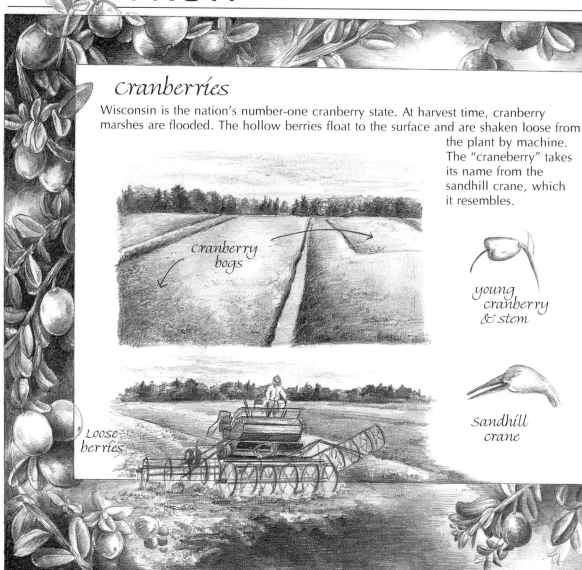

cranberry bogs

young cranberry & stem

Loose berries

sandhill crane

## cherries

Cherries are grown in Door County, where the climate is moderated by Lake Michigan.

## Apples

Wisconsin's climate gives apples good flavor and keeping qualities. You'll find orchards where the climate is not so harsh: primarily near the Great Lakes in Door and Bayfield counties, and on the ridges above the Kickapoo Valley.

# SPECIALTY CROPS

*Most likely* the mint in your toothpaste came from Wisconsin. Look for mint growing adjacent to Interstate 94 between Madison and Milwaukee and near Montello, Pardeeville, Sun Prairie, Beaver Dam, Fort Atkinson and Whitewater. Another specialty crop is tobacco, which has been grown in Wisconsin for more than a century. Today, much of it is used for cigars and chewing tobacco.

Mint

Tobacco

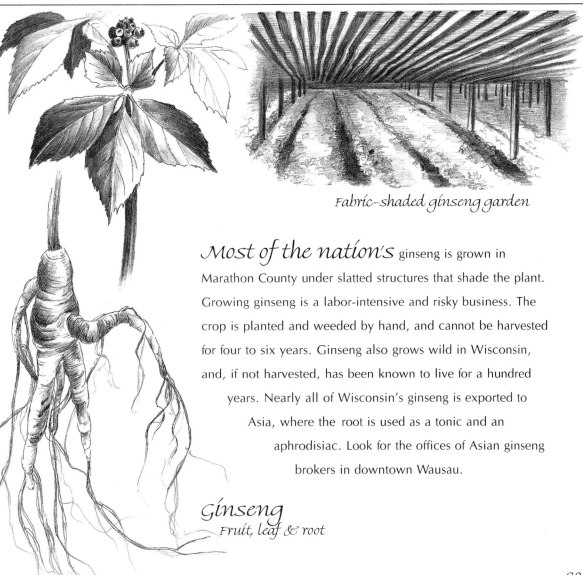

*Fabric-shaded ginseng garden*

*Most of the nation's* ginseng is grown in Marathon County under slatted structures that shade the plant. Growing ginseng is a labor-intensive and risky business. The crop is planted and weeded by hand, and cannot be harvested for four to six years. Ginseng also grows wild in Wisconsin, and, if not harvested, has been known to live for a hundred years. Nearly all of Wisconsin's ginseng is exported to Asia, where the root is used as a tonic and an aphrodisiac. Look for the offices of Asian ginseng brokers in downtown Wausau.

*Ginseng*
*Fruit, leaf & root*

# FORESTRY PRODUCTS

## Pulpwood

Wisconsin is the nation's number-one paper producer. In northern and central Wisconsin, you'll see piles of small-diameter logs in 8-foot lengths waiting to be trucked to paper factories.

## christmas trees

Large Christmas tree producers are found in the central region of the state. Trees grow six to 10 years before being cut.

*sealed plastic bag*
*(keeps debris out of fresh sap)*

## Maple syrup

You'll find the big maple syrup producers in a 50-mile-wide band across the central part of the state, from Pierce County to Langlade County, where the maple woods are thick. Trees are tapped in March, and the sap is boiled down in stainless-steel evaporators. It takes 40 gallons of sap to produce one gallon of syrup.

# Farm Animals

# FARM ANIMALS

Wisconsin is the land of the dairy cow. In fact, it has more dairy cattle than any other state in the nation—1.5 million head. Dairy cows are found throughout Wisconsin, but you'll see fewer of them in the far north, where longer winters and a shorter growing season make it more difficult to grow cow feed.

## The Dairy Cow

An average Holstein cow weighs about 1,500 pounds, drinks 35 gallons of water, and eats 20 pounds of grain and 35 pounds of hay and silage per day. A 150-pound person drinking and eating at the same rate would consume 14 quarts of water and 5 pounds of food—that's like eating 22 quarter-pound hamburgers. With four stomachs, the dairy cow efficiently converts grass and hay into milk. Even when a cow isn't eating, she is usually chewing "her cud," bringing food back into her mouth from her first stomach and chewing it a second time.

With all of that drinking, eating and cud chewing, the average cow produces about six gallons of milk each day. She also gives birth to a calf each year. A cow is milked at least twice a day, every day. No time off for weekends or vacations.

Not every dairy animal is a cow. Cows are female, they give milk, and they've given birth to one or more calves. A calf is a baby and may be either male or female. Calves, when they are born, may weigh up to 100 pounds and are able to stand and walk a few minutes after birth.

Bulls are not cows, just as men are not women. Bulls are taller and heavier than cows. But chances are you won't see a dairy bull in a pasture. Most dairy farmers breed their cows with artificial insemination because it's more convenient and it gives them access to the highest quality bulls. Bulls are housed in facilities around the country that are called bull studs. Their semen is collected and frozen, and then transported to the dairy farm where a technician inseminates the cows.

A heifer is a young female that has not yet given birth to a calf. A steer is a castrated bull; some farmers raise them for beef. A veal calf, usually a bull calf that the farmer sells to a veal producer, is milk fed until it is marketed as veal. Young stock is a catch-all term for all animals that have not reached breeding age.

The term "dairy cattle" includes all categories—cows, bulls, heifers, calves, steers. "Bovine" is a general term that refers to all dairy cattle and beef cattle, as well. "Herd" refers to a collection of dairy or beef animals.

Some farmers call their cows by yelling, "Come boss, come boss." The word has nothing to do with power and position, and everything to do with Latin. The Latin word for cow is *bos*. So when a farmer calls "Come boss," he is really calling his cows in Latin, although he may not know it.

## Holstein

It is easy to conclude that there is but one kind of dairy cow—the Holstein. Clearly, Holsteins are the predominant breed, making up some 93 percent of all dairy cows in the state. They are black and white; some are nearly all white or all black, but most have a pattern. The word "Holstein" is pronounced in two ways: Some say "hole-steen" and some say "hole-stine." And a few say "Holstein-Fresian." Holsteins come from the Netherlands (the province of West Friesland and North Holland). They came to this country with the Dutch who settled New Amsterdam, now New York, about 1630.

The Holstein breed is well known for the large quantities of milk it produces. Another reason Holstein cattle have become so popular is that they naturally produce milk that is lower in fat. Holstein cows are also "good feeders," meaning they are not fussy about what they eat. They consume large quantities of hay, silage and grain, and seem to enjoy grazing in a good pasture.

## Jersey

Jersey cow numbers (75,000) are increasing in Wisconsin but are still a far distant second to the Holsteins. Jerseys are the smallest of all the dairy breeds, weighing about 1,000 pounds at maturity.

# FARM ANIMALS

Some people argue that Jerseys are the most beautiful of all dairy cows. They are brown, tan or cream in color, and usually have a black tail, black hoofs and black nose.

Jersey milk, in contrast to Holstein milk, is naturally high in butterfat. If it is cream you want, a Jersey cow should be your choice. Total milk production is considerably lower than that of a Holstein, however. The Jersey cow comes from the Isle of Jersey, one of the Channel Islands about 70 miles off the coast of England. The first Jerseys were imported to this country about 1815. In Wisconsin, Jerseys are found most often in the southwest region.

## Brown Swiss

Brown Swiss are an old dairy breed. Present-day Brown Swiss cattle are descendants of animals raised in the valleys and mountain slopes of Switzerland since before written historic records. The name comes from the Canton of Schwyz, which had the reputation for the best Brown Cattle. Originally, Brown Swiss cattle were triple purpose. They were used for milk, for meat and as draft animals.

Brown Swiss cows, when mature, weigh between 1,400 and 1,500 pounds. In color they are similar to Jerseys, but because they are so much larger than a Jersey it is easy to tell the two breeds apart. Brown Swiss are rugged and docile.

Henry M. Clarke of Belmont, Massachusetts, is credited with importing the first Brown Swiss to this country in the winter of 1869-1870. By the late 1800s, Brown Swiss cattle were found throughout the United States.

## Guernsey

Today considered a minor dairy cattle breed, Guernseys (pronounced GERN-zees) were once found widely across the state. They originated on the Isle of Guernsey in the English Channel and were imported to the United States in 1830. A Guernsey cow looks like a small Holstein with a red and white coat. A mature cow weighs about 1,100 pounds. Guernseys produce high-butterfat milk, which is yellowish in color. "Golden

Guernsey Milk" is a copyrighted trademark for the American Guernsey Cattle Club.

## Ayrshire

Ayrshires (AIR-shirs) represent about 1.5 percent of the dairy cattle in the state, the lowest percentage of all breeds. They are hardy cattle, cherry-red and white in color. A mature Ayrshire cow weighs about 1,200 pounds. Ayrshires originated in Ayr, Scotland. Scottish settlers in Canada imported the first Ayrshires to North America in 1822.

## Beef Cattle

Determining what is and what is not a beef animal can be tricky. The easy definition of beef is "an animal raised for its meat." Beef animals include dairy steers and dairy cows and bulls that are fattened and sold for their meat, so what looks like a dairy animal may actually be a beef animal—it all depends on its intended use.

Beef cattle, those raised only for meat and not for dairy purposes, include several distinct breeds. In terms of conformation, beef cattle are wider, deeper and thicker than dairy cattle.

Beef breeds long popular on Wisconsin farms are Angus (AN-gus), Hereford (HER-furd) and Shorthorn. Because of increasing interest in lean meat and in animals that gain weight rapidly, several beef breeds recently have been introduced from Europe: Charolais (shar-o-LAY), Simmental (ZIM-men-tal), Normande, and Limousin (Lim-eh-ZEN).

Beef farmers have discovered that through cross-breeding, animals grow faster and produce leaner meat. As a result, Wisconsin beef animals are often a cross between breeds, and it is often impossible to name the beef breed when a herd is spotted in a pasture, or at a feed bunker in a feed yard.

## Pigs

Wisconsin has more than a million pigs, most of them spread out across the lower one-third of the state. A million may sound like a lot of porkers, but the state of Iowa

# FARM ANIMALS

has more than 14 million pigs.

Pigs, also known as hogs, have not had good press. Even the words have been maligned. When you eat too much, you are a pig. When you enjoy a special food, you're "pigging-out." When you drive too close to the center line, you're "hogging the road." If your congressional representative finds money to construct something in your state, it's called "pork." If you're living too prosperously, you're living "high on the hog." On the positive side, if you're driving a Harley-Davidson Hog, then you've arrived—at least in the mind of some motorcycle owners.

Popular pork products are ham, bacon, pork chops and pork roasts. Less well-known is the fact that during war years, pig fat (lard) was used to make nitroglycerine. Today, pigs provide insulin for the treatment of diabetes, heart valves to replace diseased human hearts, skin for treating severe burn victims, and leather for footballs and other sporting equipment, shoes, handbags and upholstery. Indeed, hog industry people claim that they use "everything but the oink."

There is some hog language to keep straight. A pig is not just a pig, although a pig may be called a hog (not because it eats too much, but because it is an accurate label). A mature pig that has given birth to a litter of little pigs is called a sow. A mature male pig is a boar, but almost never boring; caretakers are always careful when feeding and moving them, as they are with all male farm animals. Some boar pigs weigh 1,000 pounds and bear no resemblance to the "cute little pigs" that they once were.

A gilt is a female pig before giving birth. A barrow is a castrated male pig that is raised solely for meat production. Barrows grow faster than boars, and are much more docile and easy to care for. Little pigs may be called piglets or, merely, little pigs. Feeder pigs are of either sex, weigh about 40 pounds, and are sold to farmers who feed them until they reach market weight.

Fifty years ago, lard was the main cooking fat used in this country, and in those days pigs produced lots of it. No more. Through selective breeding, hogs have slimmed down to the point where a 3-ounce serving of roast pork tenderloin has only one gram of fat more than a comparable serving of roast chicken breast.

There are eight standard hog breeds, although many farmers will raise cross-breeds—mixtures of two or more standard breeds: Berkshires, Chester Whites, Durocs, Hampshires, Landrace, Poland Chinas, Spots (once called Spotted Poland Chinas) and Yorkshires.

## Sheep

Wisconsin is not a major sheep-raising state, ranking 25th in the nation. Texas is first. About 2,500 Wisconsin farmers raise 80,000 sheep and lambs.

Some sheep language: A ewe, pronounced "you," is a female sheep that has given birth to a lamb, which is a baby sheep of either sex. A ram, sometimes called a buck, is a mature male sheep. A wether, pronounced "weather," is a male sheep castrated before sexual maturity.

Sheep are raised for meat and wool. They graze grass much closer to the ground than cattle. Less choosy about their food, they will eat weeds that other livestock leave. Depending on the breed, a mature ewe will weigh about 200 pounds. A mature ram may weigh 275 pounds or more.

Popular sheep breeds include Suffolks, Targhees, Hampshires and Dorsets. Other sheep breeds include Corriedales and Columbias.

## Horses

Here is some basic horse information. The height of a horse is measured in "hands." A hand equals 4 inches. Thus, a horse standing 16 hands is 64 inches tall. A mare is a mature female that has given birth to a foal, either male or female. A mature male is a stallion or a stud. Sometimes you'll see that a stallion is standing at stud, which means his owner has made him available for breeding purposes. A filly is a young female horse. A gelding is a castrated male horse.

Horses come in a variety of colors, and each color has a special name. A gray is white. A bay is red-brown to dark brown. A chestnut is reddish gold. A palomino has

# FARM ANIMALS

a gold coat, the color of a new penny, with a white mane and tail. Black is black. Dapple gray means there are rings of dark gray on a white coat. Paint refers to large irregular patches of white and any other color except black. Spot means white with spots of various colors over the hips. (Appaloosa riding horses are a good example.) So, when you see a white horse in a field, you should say, "Look at that interesting gray horse," or, if the gray horse has a colt beside it, you could go further and say, "Look at that gray mare, with that cute little colt."

Two major types of horses are draft horses and riding/carriage horses. The most popular draft horse breeds in Wisconsin are Belgian, Percheron and Clydesdale. All three breeds are about 16 hands high, and may weigh up to 2,000 pounds each. Try to avoid having one step on your foot. Belgians originated in Belgium, Percherons came from France, and Clydesdales were bred in Scotland.

Of the various riding/carriage horse breeds, many have roots in the Arabian breed. Arabians are even the principal foundation breed for today's Thoroughbreds (race horses). These swift and sure-footed animals were developed by the nomadic Bedouin tribes in the deserts of North Africa. Arabian horses are known for stamina, endurance, and loyalty.

An Arabian horse carries its tail high and has widely spaced eyes and a dished forehead with a small tapered muzzle, and is one of the most beautiful of all horse breeds. Arabians stand about 14 hands high. The quarter horse is Wisconsin's most popular riding horse. Claimed as the first all-American breed, some say it is the most popular horse in the world. The name "quarter horse" refers to the fact that settlers raced these animals for a quarter of a mile. They have the ability to sprint faster than any other breed over this distance. Their heads are short and wide, they stand 14 to 15 hands high, and they have large, muscular hind quarters.

Other popular riding/carriage horse breeds include appaloosa, saddlebred and Morgan.

## Other Farm Animals

Wisconsin produces more ranch mink, about 700,000 pelts per year, than any other state in the nation. To identify a mink ranch, look for many small shelters enclosed by a fence. They are found primarily in central and northern Wisconsin.

Wisconsin is second only to California in milk production from dairy goats. Three Wisconsin cheese factories buy goat milk for cheese production. A dairy goat herd will range from four or five hand-milked goats to several hundred animals.

A female goat is a doe, a male is a buck, and the little ones are called kids. Nubian goats are of Oriental origin, long-legged and hardy. Alpines originated in the Alps and were brought to the U.S. from France. They are hardy, adaptable animals that thrive in almost any climate. Oberhasli are Swiss dairy goats.

Some Wisconsin farmers have begun raising llamas, primarily for their wool, which is feather-soft and oil free. Many weavers prefer it. Llamas also are raised as family pets, as guard llamas for sheep flocks, and for carrying loads. Llamas consume much less feed than beef or dairy cattle. They eat only about one 40-pound bale of hay per week, and up to five llamas can graze on one acre of land.

Alpacas, smaller cousins of llamas, have become popular in the Midwest, but their numbers are still much smaller than llamas. Alpacas are raised primarily for their wool. While llamas are individualistic, alpacas are herd oriented. They don't like to be alone, and so are not used as guard or pack animals.

Bison, or buffaloes, are raised by several Wisconsin farmers for their meat, which is low in fat content. A few farmers raise elk and deer for their meat. Emus and ostriches are also sold for meat and as breeding animals.

Honeybees are important to Wisconsin's agricultural economy. They pollinate cranberries and other fruit crops, and, of course, make honey. Wisconsin has about 6,000 beekeepers. Due to bee diseases and low honey prices, the number of beekeepers has decreased in recent years. Bees are housed in what appear to be stacks of wooden boxes, often near the edge of a woodlot. The removable upper boxes of a bee hive are called supers. To spot a honey producer, look for a "Honey for Sale" sign near the road.

# DAIRY COWS

Holstein &
minutes-old calf

*wisconsin has* more

dairy cattle than any other state in the nation—

1.5 million head. Ninety-three percent of these are Holsteins.

Cows of this breed produce large quantities of lower-fat milk and are not fussy about what

they eat. Holsteins are also very docile animals, perhaps due to the fact that in the Netherlands,

where the breed was developed, they often slept under the same roof as the family. Holsteins

are easily identified by their black-and-white markings.

# DAIRY COWS

Jersey

Brown Swiss

Jersey   Guernsey   Holstein   Ayrshire   Brown Swiss

**The Jersey** is the smallest of the dairy breeds and, some say, the most beautiful. Jersey cows are brown, tan or cream in color and usually have a black tail, black hoofs and a black nose. Jersey milk has a high butterfat content. You are most apt to see Jerseys in the southwestern part of the state. Brown Swiss cows resemble Jerseys in color but are much larger. Today's cattle are descended from animals raised in Switzerland before written historic records. Guernseys have a red and white coat. The term "Golden Guernsey" was coined to draw attention to the characteristic golden color of Guernsey milk. Ayrshire cattle are cherry-red and white in color, and are the least common breed in Wisconsin.

Guernsey

Ayrshire

# BEEF CATTLE

Beef cattle, raised only for their meat, are wider, deeper and thicker than dairy cattle. Because Wisconsin beef animals are often cross-breeds, it can be difficult to identify a specific breed.

## Hereford

Herefords are red and white and have relatively long legs. Rugged animals, they are able to withstand extreme weather, are well suited to rough terrain, and can cover long distances to find a meal. The breed originated in England.

## Black Angus

Black Angus are solid black in color. They have short legs and are very boxy in appearance. The breed originated in Scotland. In the past, Angus meat was prized because it is well marbled. In contrast to Herefords, Angus do better in confined areas.

## Shorthorns

Shorthorns come in a variety of colors, ranging from red to cream. They stand taller than Angus but are not as rugged as Herefords. Shorthorns were popular with pioneers because they produced both meat and milk, and could pull a plow or a wagon. They are considered less efficient "converters" of feed to meat; in other words, they require more feed than other breeds to produce the same quantity of meat.

# BEEF CATTLE

## Limousin

Limousin cattle are unusually sturdy, native to south-central France where they were kept outside year-round and used as beasts of burden. These golden-red animals, which arrived in the U.S. in 1975, are similar in appearance to cattle depicted in cave drawings in France that are 20,000 years old.

## Normande

Normande, also of French origin, are large in size and black and white in color.

## charolais

Charolais, another French import, are large animals, white or cream-colored, with appreciable pigmentation.

## simmental

Simmental originated in Switzerland and became popular in the U.S. in the 1960s. They are red with white markings around the face.

# PIGS

*The pig was* one of the first animals to be domesticated, probably around 7,000 B.C. At one time, every dairy farmer raised a few pigs, not only to provide food for the family but to bring in extra income, a practice that resulted in the pig's nickname, "Mortgage Lifter." Pigs grow fast. Gestation time for hogs is 112 days. A little pig will grow to 240 pounds (market size) in five months. Hampshire pigs are black with a white band around the shoulders and legs. Berkshires are also black but their legs are only partially white. Yorkshires are all white and have a long snout. Poland China pigs look like Berkshires but have floppy ears.

*Hampshire*

*Berkshire*

*Yorkshire*

Poland China

# HORSES

*Belgian*

*Percheron*

## Wisconsin horses

fall into two major categories: draft horses, used for farm work, and riding or carriage horses. The most common draft horse breeds are Belgian, Percheron and Clydesdale. Draft horses are enormous animals, standing about 16 hands (64 inches) tall and weighing up to a ton. The quarter horse is Wisconsin's most popular riding horse. It is so named because settlers raced these animals for a quarter mile. Quarter horses cover this distance faster than any other breed of horse.

*Quarter horse*

# SHEEP

Wisconsin is not a sheep-raising state. Still, about 2,500 Wisconsin farmers raise 80,000 sheep and lambs.

## Dorset

Dorset sheep are all white; some have horns and some do not. They are good producers of both wool and meat. Like all sheep, they are not choosy about what they eat and will eat weeds other livestock walk past.

## Suffolk

Suffolks, popular in Wisconsin, are white with a black wool-free head and black wool-free legs.

## Hampshire

Hampshires also are white with a black face and legs. Unlike Suffolks, Hampshires have wool growing on top of their head.

## Targhee

One of America's youngest breeds, the Targhee was developed in Idaho beginning in the 1920s, and is named after the national forest in which the animals grazed during the summer. Targhee sheep are grayish-white with a white face.

# GOATS, ALPACAS & LLAMAS

*Wisconsin ranks* second in the nation, behind California, in milk production from dairy goats. There are many breeds of goats. Nubians, considered "aristocratic" in appearance and Oriental in origin, are usually black, red or tan, sometimes combined with white. Alpines, which originated in the Alps, range in color from white to shades of gray, brown, red and black.

*Nubian goat*

*Alpine goat*

Llama

Alpaca

**Llamas are** low-maintenance animals,
eating just one bale of hay per week. They produce soft,
oil-free wool. Llamas also guard sheep and make good
pack animals and family pets. Alpacas are related to llamas,
but are smaller. They are raised primarily for their wool.

117

# OTHER FARM ANIMALS

*Ostriches and emus* are grown primarily for their red meat, which is low in fat. A quarter-pound serving of emu meat, for example, provides 23 grams of protein, 109 calories and less than two grams of fat. In contrast, a quarter-pound of beef provides 20 grams of protein, 225 calories and 15 grams of fat. The ostrich, the world's largest bird, is native to Africa. The emu, the world's second-largest bird, is native to Australia.

ostrich

Emu

**Bison, or buffaloes,** are raised by several Wisconsin farmers for their meat, which is low in fat content. You'll see these animals behind tall fences erected to keep them from escaping.

## Honeybees

Honeybees produce honey, of course, but they also aid in the pollination of fruit crops, such as cranberries.

*A beekeeper working in his honey yard.*

*Bees are housed in what appear to be stacks of wooden boxes. Look for them near the edge of a woodlot.*

planting
and
Harvesting

# PLANTING & HARVESTING

## Soil Preparation

Wisconsin fields are empty during the winter, except perhaps for a tractor pulling a manure spreader. But by April, when the snow has melted and the soil warmed, farmers are preparing the soil for planting.

Traditionally, farmers plow (in either fall or spring) and disk the soil, then drag, or smooth, it. Much farmland is still prepared this way. Each plow bottom is 16 inches wide. A two-bottom plow, common 40 years ago but still used today, turns less than 3 feet of soil each time across the field. A 12-bottom plow—making 12 furrows with one trip—will turn a strip of soil 16 feet wide at one time.

A disk harrow has rotating disks set a foot or less apart on a shaft. As the individual disks turn, they cut the soil, mix and smooth it. Modern disk harrows range in width from 6 feet to 24 feet. The larger ones have tires for transport, and the especially large ones fold into the air so they can be pulled on the road.

A drag has many spike teeth that dig into the ground, smoothing the ridges created by the disk harrow. A drag is used if the farmer wants an even surface—if he is sowing alfalfa seed, for instance, and wants a smooth hayfield. An older drag may cover 16 feet with each pass across a field; today's newer drags may cover 50 feet.

Soil for corn may be fall or spring plowed, chisel plowed or deep disked, or the farmer may follow a practice called no-till. A chisel plow does not turn the soil but loosens it in preparation for planting. Deep disking provides similar results. No-till means the farmer plants corn in the stubble of last year's crop, with little disturbance of the soil. The advantage of no-till farming is that it helps prevent water and wind erosion. A disadvantage is that herbicides and pesticides are necessary to control weed and insect pests.

## Planting

Corn is planted with a corn planter, a machine that places the corn seeds and fertilizer in rows. The machine may plant four rows, six rows or even 12 rows at a time.

The rows are usually about 30 inches apart so that a farmer can drive between them with a cultivator to remove weeds, or pull a weed sprayer. Soybeans are planted with a corn planter that has special plates to accommodate the soybean seed, or with a grain drill specially designed for soybean planting.

Grain—wheat, oats, barley, rye—is sowed with a grain drill. The drill, a machine consisting of disks a few inches apart, opens the soil and places the grain in the ground. Some drills also have attachments so that alfalfa, clover and other hay crops may be planted at the same time. Grain drills, like corn planters, come in various sizes. They vary from 12 feet wide to 35 feet (the latter model folds for transport). Occasionally, hay crops are planted directly with a grass seeder that may plant 15 or 20 feet at a time.

## caring for crops

Grain crops require little attention from the time they are planted until they are harvested. Corn and vegetable crops such as potatoes, green beans, beets and cucumbers require considerable looking after while they are growing.

Corn does not compete well with weeds, especially when it is small. If not removed, the weeds will win. To control weeds, farmers cultivate and/or spray. A weed sprayer is a large, gangly machine with booms sticking out from either side. A weed killer—herbicide—is sprayed on the cornfields in a fine mist. The corn plant itself is tolerant of the herbicide.

Because of concerns about chemicals seeping into the groundwater, some farmers have returned to mechanical weed control. When the corn plants are young, a tractor pulls a cultivator slowly between the rows, loosening the soil and removing the weeds. Cultivators cultivate two to eight or more rows with one trip across the field. Once the corn is knee high, its leaves shade the spaces between the rows, preventing weed growth.

In the vegetable growing areas of the state, especially where green beans and potatoes are grown, it is not uncommon for farmers to spray their crops from airplanes. An aerial spray plane, with spray booms attached to its underbelly, flies a few feet

# PLANTING & HARVESTING

above the crop. To watch a spray-plane pilot work is like watching an air show as the plane roars almost straight up into the air at the end of a crop row (generally to avoid some electric wires or trees), banks tightly, dives to within a few feet of the ground, then levels off for another spraying run. The pilot is guided by white cloth markers in the field—spot the markers and you will know that the field has been aerial sprayed, or is scheduled to be sprayed.

Cucumbers require hand hoeing, a time-honored way of controlling weeds. Today, most hand hoeing is done by migrant workers who come to Wisconsin in early summer and stay through the harvesting season.

Irrigation of vegetable crops is common in many parts of Wisconsin today, especially near Spring Green and in the central sands area south of Stevens Point. An irrigation system is impossible to miss. It consists of a long pipe supported by tall rubber tires, with nozzles spaced every few inches along the pipe that spray water directly on the plants. A typical irrigation system will irrigate a 160-acre field by moving slowly all the way around it. Water for the irrigation system usually comes from a well, drilled to a depth of 150 to 400 feet. During especially dry weather, it is not uncommon to see irrigation systems operating 24 hours a day, everyday, until it rains. It is also possible for farmers to add fertilizer and pesticides to the irrigation water, saving repeated trips across the field. Modern-day irrigation systems use computers to control irrigation operations.

## Harvesting

Hay is the first crop harvested, sometimes beginning as early as mid-May and continuing into June. Additional hay harvesting takes place throughout the summer, as second and third crops become ready. If there is sufficient rain in April, hay grows rapidly.

Some hayfields are cut for green feeding. A farmer, with a forage harvester and a portable feed bunker toted behind, cuts the fresh alfalfa, blows it into the feed bunker and then hauls it to the feedlot for immediate consumption by the cattle. For some farmers, this is an everyday task throughout the growing season.

Much of Wisconsin's hay crop is made into silage. The hay is cut with a hay conditioner and dried slightly. It is then cut again into short lengths with a forage harvester, blown into a forage wagon and hauled to the silo, where it is stored.

To make dry hay, four steps are involved: cutting, drying, baling and storing. For years, hay was cut with a sickle-bar mower, which works like multiple pairs of scissors. Modern-day sickle-bar mowers, called haybines, swathers or hay conditioners, cut the hay, crush the stems for faster drying and then put the hay into long rows about 2 feet high, where they await the baler. Haybines are tractor pulled or, sometimes, self-propelled. A newer machine, called a disc-mower or discbine, cuts the hay with small, free-swinging knives on whirling discs. The discbine is less likely to clog, allowing the farmer to mow more hay in less time.

After hay is cut, it dries for several hours in the field. Ideal drying conditions are sunshine and low humidity—thus the phrase, "make hay while the sun shines." With ideal conditions, hay will dry sufficiently for baling in a day. Nothing in the countryside smells finer than drying hay.

Hay rakes are tractor-pulled machines that turn and gather the drying hay into long ropes for baling. Hay balers come in various styles. Some make square bales that weigh between 35 and 60 pounds. A square-bale baler may (1) drop the bales on the ground, (2) push the finished bales up a chute to a wagon where farm hands load them (100 or more bales per wagon load), or (3) toss the bales into a wagon that has sides and a back. At the barn, the bales are carried to the barn's hay mow with an elevator.

Other balers make round bales that weigh between 600 pounds and a ton. These huge round bales are sometimes left in the field until they are fed to cattle. More often, they are moved to the sides of the field with special tractor-operated bale haulers, or toted to the farmstead where they are stored in large open-sided sheds.

Peas are harvested in early summer. Huge tractor-pulled or self-propelled pea viners work their way across the pea fields. Often, several work together.

# PLANTING & HARVESTING

In mid- to late summer, mechanical bean pickers harvest green beans. As with peas, several of the machines work together. It is not unusual, especially when traveling the secondary roads of Wisconsin, to come upon a convoy of pea viners or mechanical bean pickers moving from one field to another.

Cucumber harvesting has defied machines. Migrant workers, most of whom are Mexican-Americans from south Texas, pick almost all of Wisconsin's cucumber crop. In late July and August, you'll see them bending over the ground-hugging plants, filling bag after bag with the green, spiny vegetable. Occasionally, you'll spot migrant worker camps, clusters of small buildings where families live while they are working in the fields.

By late July and early August, the oat crop is ready for harvest. Combines, some self-propelled and some pulled by tractors, harvest the grain. The machine is called a combine because it combines several harvesting functions that for years were done separately. A combine cuts the crop, threshes it (separates the grain kernels from the straw) and deposits the straw back on the land. Many farmers follow the combine with a hay rake and a hay baler to save the oat straw. Oat straw is widely used as bedding for dairy cows when they are kept in the barn.

By late August, the potato harvest is in full swing, with mechanical potato diggers moving across the potato fields, tumbling the freshly dug tubers into potato trucks. Sweet corn harvest begins in August, too. Mechanical corn pickers move across the green fields, snapping the ears of sweet corn from their stalks and depositing them into wagons.

Field corn for silage is also harvested in late August, while the corn plant is still green and moist enough to ferment. Forage harvesters move down the rows, cutting the corn plants into small pieces and blowing them into a forage wagon. The corn is unloaded into a machine that blows it into the silo.

The grain corn harvest usually begins in October, after the first killing frosts, which helps dry down the corn plant. Two harvesting approaches are widely used. The first involves a corn picker that moves along the rows, snaps off the dry corn ears and removes the husks. The cob corn, as it is called, is dropped into a wagon that follows behind the corn picker. When the wagon is full, it is pulled to the farmstead, and the corn stored in a corn crib.

With the second method, a corn combine, somewhat similar in appearance to a corn picker, moves along the rows and snaps off the corn ears. Unlike the corn picker, however, the corn combine shells the corn seeds from the cobs, and the shelled corn is collected in a tank on the top of the combine. When filled, the combine dumps its load of freshly shelled corn in a truck or a tractor-pulled wagon. The shelled corn is hauled to the farmstead where it is dried and stored in bins.

The cranberry harvest begins in October, as does the harvesting of Christmas trees. Christmas tree harvest reaches its peak in early November. Drive by a Christmas tree processing center in central Wisconsin at that time, and you'll see thousands of trees piled high, awaiting shipment to Christmas tree lots throughout the country.

## Tractors

At one time a farmer had only one tractor for planting, harvesting and a host of other tasks. Today, a farmer will own several tractors, small, large, old and new. Unlike automobiles, farm tractors last a long time. It is common to see tractors that were built in the 1940s and 1950s working in Wisconsin fields.

The farmer driving a 1950s John Deere or Farmall H sits out in the open, exposed to the elements. In a 1990s tractor, the farmer sits in an air-conditioned cab with a high-output stereo system, and a weather-band radio.

Tractors come in several colors; red, green, blue and orange are the most common. While automobile makers sell cars and trucks in many colors, farm implement manufacturers stick to one. Green equals John Deere, red means Case IH, Ford tractors are blue, and Agco Allis are orange. Farmers develop a fierce loyalty to tractor manufacturers. Often, you'll see farming equipment all of one color on a farm.

# TRACTORS

John Deere
1950s

Ford
1940s

*You'll see just* about every kind of tractor made since 1945 still operating on Wisconsin farms. Tractors of the same vintage tend to look alike, but you can usually identify a machine's manufacturer by its color. John Deere tractors are green. Older Ford tractors are gray; newer ones are blue. International Harvesters are red. Massey Fergusons also are red. Farmers typically own several tractors. Older, smaller tractors are used for small jobs, and larger ones for big jobs.

International Harvester 1960s

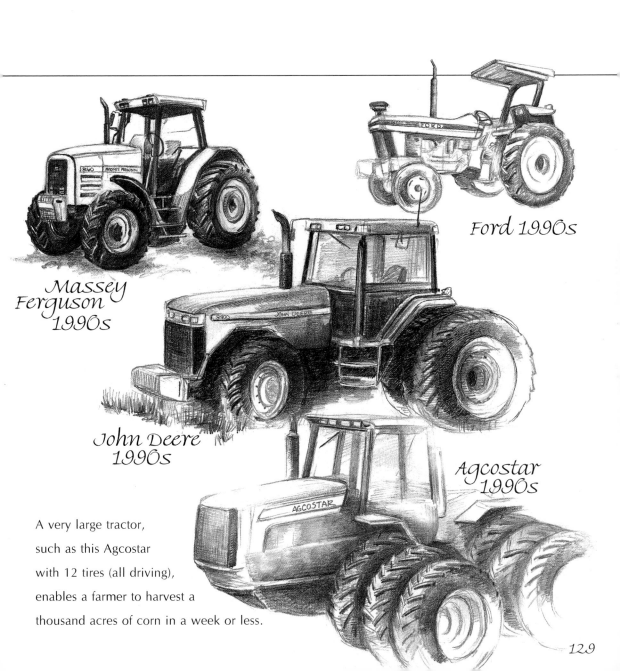

Massey
Ferguson
1990s

Ford 1990s

John Deere
1990s

Agcostar
1990s

A very large tractor,
such as this Agcostar
with 12 tires (all driving),
enables a farmer to harvest a
thousand acres of corn in a week or less.

129

# SPRING PLANTING

Farmers generally prepare soil by plowing, disking and, sometimes, dragging, which smoothes the field. Planting requires different equipment for different crops.

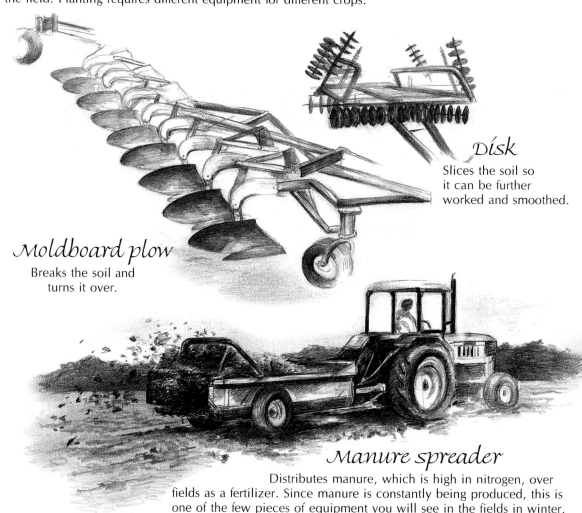

### Disk
Slices the soil so it can be further worked and smoothed.

### Moldboard plow
Breaks the soil and turns it over.

### Manure spreader
Distributes manure, which is high in nitrogen, over fields as a fertilizer. Since manure is constantly being produced, this is one of the few pieces of equipment you will see in the fields in winter.

**Honey wagon** Distributes liquid manure over fields as a fertilizer. The smell from a "honey" wagon is one you will never forget.

## Drill

Opens a trench, drops a seed (usually oat, wheat, rye or barley), covers the hole, and places fertilizer in the soil, all in one pass.

## corn planter

Plants two to 10 rows of corn at a time The "stick" at the end makes a mark that the farmer will follow on his return pass so that rows are evenly spaced.

## Potato planter

A common sight in central Wisconsin and sections of northern Wisconsin. Has larger seed boxes, and usually plants fewer rows than a corn planter.

# SUMMER WORK

During the summer, farmers control weeds either by
spraying herbicides on the fields or removing
weeds mechanically with a cultivator.

*spraying for weeds*

*cultivating*

## Irrigation system

An irrigation rig waters 160 acres in one sweep.
On the most modern models, a computer controls
the rate of speed, direction and the amount of water applied.
Because irrigation systems apply water to a square field in a
circular pattern, you will often see drought-tolerant crops
growing in the corners of an irrigated field.

# HARVESTING HAY

*Tractor-pulled
hay conditioner*

*Hay baler making round bales*

*Square bales*

*Handling round bales*

**Hay is dried** plant material used for feeding cattle, horses, sheep and goats. (Pigs don't eat hay because their single stomach cannot digest it.) About 90 percent of hay is alfalfa, but it may be clover or timothy. Traditionally, hay was cut with a sickle mower, then raked with either a straight or a curly rake. Today, hay is most commonly cut, crushed and heaped into rows, called "windrows," all in one operation with a machine called a hay conditioner. Hay may be baled square or round. Square bales are usually small, weighing 40 to 60 pounds. Round bales may be small or large—some are 10 feet in diameter and weigh 1,500 pounds. A forage harvester cuts hay while it is green and blows it into a wagon. It is fed immediately to cattle, a practice known as "green feeding."

*Hay rake*

*Tractor-pulled forage harvester*

135

# HARVESTING FIELD CORN & SMALL GRAINS

*corn picker*

*corn combine*

*Self-propelled combine*

*Forage harvester*

*A corn picker* picks an ear of corn whole, husks it and drops it into a wagon that is pulled behind it. A combine "combines" a number of operations. A corn combine strips corn ears from the plant and husks and shells the corn. A combine used with wheat, oats, rye and barley cuts the grain, threshes it (that is, separates the grain from the straw), deposits the straw on the ground and drops the grain in a bin. A forage harvester cuts corn plants to be stored in a silo for silage. Combines are much larger machines than forage harvesters.

# HARVESTING VEGETABLES & TOBACCO

Wisconsin's vegetable crop is huge. From early summer till fall, you will see machines and, in some instances, migrant workers in the fields harvesting vegetables to be taken to the canneries. The country's first commercial cannery for peas, the Lakeside Packing Company, was founded in Wisconsin in 1897.

## Peas

Peas are harvested in June. A self-propelled pea viner cuts the pea vine, shucks the pods, collects the peas and drops the refuse back on the ground.

## Cucumbers

Because cucumbers bear over a period of about six weeks, they are best harvested by human hand. Migrant workers, most of whom are Mexican-Americans from south Texas, pick almost all of Wisconsin's cucumber crop. You'll see workers bent over the low-growing plants in July and August.

## Potatoes

Potatoes are harvested from August through September with a mechanical potato harvester, which digs the tubers out of the ground and deposits them in a truck.

## Tobacco

To harvest tobacco, a cash crop in a few southern and western counties, farmers chop the plants by hand, allow them to dry in the fields, then collect the leaves with a spear. The spears support the leaves in drying sheds, where they hang to further dry until around Christmas. On a foggy day, after the leaves have absorbed some moisture, they are removed, packed in a box and shipped to tobacco buyers.

Other
Rural
Buildings

# OTHER RURAL BUILDINGS

## churches

Soon after arriving in Wisconsin, settlers built churches. The first ones often were made of logs. These rustic buildings were replaced by wood-frame, brick and stone structures, many of which stand today as reminders of the state's religious heritage.

Catholic and Lutheran churches dominate Wisconsin's countryside, reflecting the major ethnic groups that settled here. The Polish, Irish, Italian, French-Canadian, Belgians, Swiss and about half of the Germans were Catholic; consequently, Wisconsin became one of the most Catholic states in the nation. Norwegians, Swedes, Danes and the half of the German population that was not Catholic were Lutheran.

The first Norwegian Lutheran Church in North America was built in Koshkonong in southern Dane County. Norwegian immigrants came to this area in 1839. They were followed, in 1844, by the Reverend J. W. C. Dietrichson, an ordained Lutheran minister from Norway. On Sept. 1, he conducted the first church services for the community in a barn. In East Koshkonong, 40 families and a few single people formed a congregation and began building a church. In West Koshkonong, 30 families and some single people did the same thing. Each constructed a log church, 36 by 28 feet. More substantial church buildings followed. Because of a doctrinal rift in the late 1800s, the congregations each split in two, and two more churches were built. Today, you can see four magnificent churches, two in East Koshkonong and two in West Koshkonong.

## Town Halls

Wisconsin was surveyed in an orderly fashion. The state was, and continues to be, divided into townships. Each township is 6 miles square and contains 36 sections of land. (A section of land is 640 acres.) Townships were clustered into counties, but counties do not have an equal number of townships.

At the time the state constitution was written, most of Wisconsin was rural. The constitution mandated that every township have a town government. As cities and villages sprung up and were incorporated, they formed their own governmental bodies.

(An incorporated village must have a population of at least 150; the minimum population for a city is 1,000.) Areas of Wisconsin that are not included in the corporate boundaries of cities and villages are still governed by their town government. When you see the name of a village and underneath it the word "unincorporated" that means the government of the village is conducted by the town of which it is a part.

The town hall is the focal point of town government. Often it is a small wooden structure, simple and without adornment. The town hall is usually located near the center of a township, and it is here that citizens of the town vote, participate in town business and attend community social activities. In the middle 1800s, when much of Wisconsin was settled, horses were the primary mode of transportation. The idea was that no farmer should have to travel more than three miles or so to reach the town hall.

## Cheese Factories

Wisconsin produces more cheese than any other state. At the time of this writing, 142 cheese plants produce about 2 billion pounds of cheese a year, more than twice as much as California, the state's closest competitor. Thirty-one percent of all cheese produced in the U.S. comes from the Badger State. Wisconsin cheesemakers make more than 250 types and varieties of cheese. They make more Italian cheese than the Italians. They also make all of the U.S.'s Limburger cheese. The sole factory producing Limburger operates in Green County.

Nearly 90 percent of all the milk produced in Wisconsin is used to manufacture cheese. Unlike butter, which uses only cream, cheesemaking uses all the milk. Ten pounds of milk is needed for one pound of cheese.

It is easy to identify an operating cheese factory; a retail cheese store is usually a part of the building. In older cheese factories, the owner lived in the building, either upstairs or in the back. Many of these factories have closed in recent years, but most of the buildings still stand. Former cheese factories are easy to identify. The buildings are often much longer than they are wide, and are often located at a crossroads.

# OTHER RURAL BUILDINGS

## One-Room Country Schools

At one time Wisconsin had more that 6,000 one-room country schools located about four miles apart throughout the countryside. Today there is one, operating on Madeline Island. But, as with cheese factories, many of the buildings still stand. Today, numerous old schools are homes; several serve as school museums, gift shops and antique stores.

One-room country schools operated with all eight grades in one room and with one teacher. There was no kindergarten. Most had outdoor toilets, no running water, and were heated with wood stoves. By the 1960s, all one-room schools were closed and the rural children were bused to consolidated schools. Often today, you will see school bus shelters in which children wait for the bus on winter mornings. The homemade shelters, sometimes only 3 or 4 feet square and only 4 or 5 feet high with a window or two, are of various shapes and colors, and are always located at the intersection of a rural driveway and the road that passes by.

## Grist Mills

Before Wisconsin became a dairy state in the late 1800s, it was a premier wheat producer and major flour-milling state. Powered by water, these early mills shipped flour to Chicago, St. Louis and other major urban areas. When selecting a mill site, the miller searched out a fast-moving stream. He then built a dam, creating a millpond that provided water for a wooden water wheel or a turbine.

The mill itself is usually two or three stories tall. Water from the millpond often flowed to the basement, confined in a metal tube called a penstock, before entering the turbine. Sometimes the water flowed in an open flume to the turbine. In either case, the water pressure turned the metal fins in the turbine, providing power for grinding.

After 1882, when the first hydroelectric plant in the country began operating in Appleton, many flour mills generated electricity for the nearby villages. Thus, village dwellers had access to electricity years before the REA provided electricity for farmers.

Some of these old flour mills still grind cattle feed, and some even generate electricity. Most, though, have stopped using water power for grinding and have replaced the turbine with an electric motor. The millponds remain, as attractive home sites and as places for community recreation.

## Deer Stands and Fish Shanties

Wisconsin has a long deer-hunting and ice-fishing tradition. Each fall, during Thanksgiving week, thousands of orange-clad hunters march into the countryside, in search of the wary whitetail.

Many hunters hunt from deer stands. The simplest deer stand is a platform, 8 or 10 feet off the ground, on which a hunter stands or sits while waiting for a deer to walk underneath. More sophisticated deer stands have roofs, walls and windows. Here the hunter sits in comfort, often warmed by a gas heater. Sometimes, he even has a portable TV to watch the Badgers and the Packers while "hunting."

Ice shanties are found on frozen lakes, often in clusters that form shanty towns. Ice fishermen sit within the four walls of their ice shanty huddled over holes they have drilled in the ice. Special ice-fishing "jig poles" are used to catch perch, bluegills, sunfish and crappies. The ice fisherman may also have a tip-up set by a larger hole outside the fishing shanty. The hope is to hook a northern pike, a fish that may weigh as much as 20 pounds, though anything over five pounds earns bragging rights. When a tip-up's red flag jerks up, the fisherman bursts out of the ice shanty, slipping and sliding to the hole, hoping he has caught the big one.

# CHURCHES

The architectural style of a church relates to the period in which it was built rather than to the theology of the congregation. In other words, gazing at a hilltop church from a distance, you cannot tell whether it is a Catholic, Lutheran, Presbyterian or Congregational house of worship. Churches do reflect Wisconsin's settlement patterns, however. As you drive around the state you will notice a preponderance of Catholic and Lutheran churches. This is because the major ethnic groups that settled here—Germans, Norwegians, Swiss, Swedes, Polish and Irish—were of those faiths.

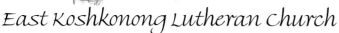

## East Koshkonong Lutheran Church

The first Norwegian Lutheran churches in North America were built in East and West Koshkonong in Dane County. The original log structures were constructed in 1844.

## First Lutheran Church,

The 1852 First Lutheran Church, on Pleasant View Road in Dane County, was one of the first German Lutheran churches to be built in Wisconsin.

## St. Augustine's Church

This Catholic Church in New Diggings is the work of Father Samuel Mazzuchelli. When Mazzuchelli arrived in Green Bay in 1830, he was the only priest west of Lake Michigan. By the time of his death, he had established 645 churches, 25 of his own building.

# CHURCHES

### St. Norbert's Church

Built in 1846, this was the first Catholic church in south-central Wisconsin. The building now standing in the town of Roxbury, a mile from the original site, replaced the 18- by 20-foot log building. It rises above the community on a slight hill and has a tall steeple that can be seen for miles.

### St. John the Baptist Church

This Catholic church in Heffron was built in 1906 to serve the large Polish community that had established itself in Portage County. Its setting is typical: All that's there is the church, the priest's house, a dance hall and a tavern.

## Wyoming Valley Church

Like all Methodist churches, this one is distinguished by its plain facade. It is located on Highway 23 between Spring Green and Dodgeville.

## Belgian Chapel

Wisconsin pioneers built chapels for family worship and to serve small rural congregations. Many wayside chapels were built by Belgian Catholic immigrants. Look for these buildings along the back roads of lower Door County.

# TOWN HALLS

*The town hall* represents the governmental seat of a town. It is here that the town board meets to discuss and vote on matters of concern to the community, such as zoning changes, snowplow purchases and road repairs. Town halls were placed in the center of a township so that farmers could get there and back within a reasonable amount of time. Modern town halls not only serve as gathering places but often house the police department, fire trucks and road maintenance equipment.

# ONE-ROOM COUNTRY SCHOOLS

*One-room schools* were a common feature of the Wisconsin countryside for 200 years. The earliest one-room schools were constructed of logs. Later, wood-frame buildings were most common, though brick and quarried rock were also used. Wisconsin was a leading state in providing public education. Under the School Law of 1848, elementary education was declared free to anyone between the ages of 4 and 20, and schools had to be open at least three months of the year. Almost all one-room country schools closed in the 1950s and 1960s when school districts consolidated and rural children were bused to schools in nearby villages and cities.

*school made of brick, south of Blanchardville*

*school made of quarried rock, near Roxbury*

# ONE-ROOM
# COUNTRY SCHOOLS

*Amish school,*
*Columbia County*

## Amish communities

frequently operate one-room schools. These buildings have neither electricity nor indoor plumbing, and depend on wood-burning stoves for heat. When school is in session, you will see the buggies that many of the children drive to school lined up in the yard. The only public one-room school still operating in Wisconsin is in La Pointe on Madeline Island in Lake Superior. You will, however, find many old school buildings still in use. Rather than see a good building go to waste, farmers often moved a school building to their farm and used it for storage.

*Red School, now a museum in Sharon*

*Interior of Red School museum*

# CHEESE FACTORIES

*Since 1910,* Wisconsin has been the nation's leading cheese producer, an industry created by hundreds of small factories. The local cheese factory era waned with the introduction of milk pickup from the farm, but you can still find many of these buildings, often neglected and sometimes converted to other uses, standing at rural crossroads. The earliest cheese factories are very small, usually of wood-frame construction, with a raised porch upon which farmers' milk was unloaded. Modernized buildings are low-slung and narrow, often with a retail store and living quarters on the second floor. Visit a cheese factory that is still operating and you are likely to discover that it has been run by the same family for several generations.

*cedar Grove cheese factory, near Plain*

# CONVERTED DAIRY BARNS

ROUND
BARN

*Round Barn restaurant,
Spring Green*

A number of Wisconsin barns have been successfully converted to nonfarm uses, testimony to their sturdy construction. How can you tell if a building that looks like a barn really was a barn? Check its beams: An old barn will have pegged beams; a modern structure's beams are bolted. Also notice the walls. An old barn's basement walls will be thick and made of fieldstone or quarried rock, while a new building will have concrete basement walls.

Don Q Inn, Dodgeville

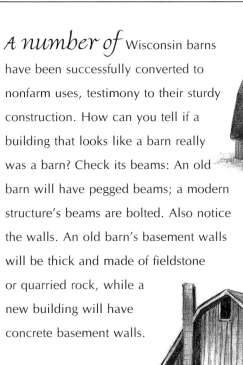

Sparby's Garden Center, Waunakee

# GRIST MILLS

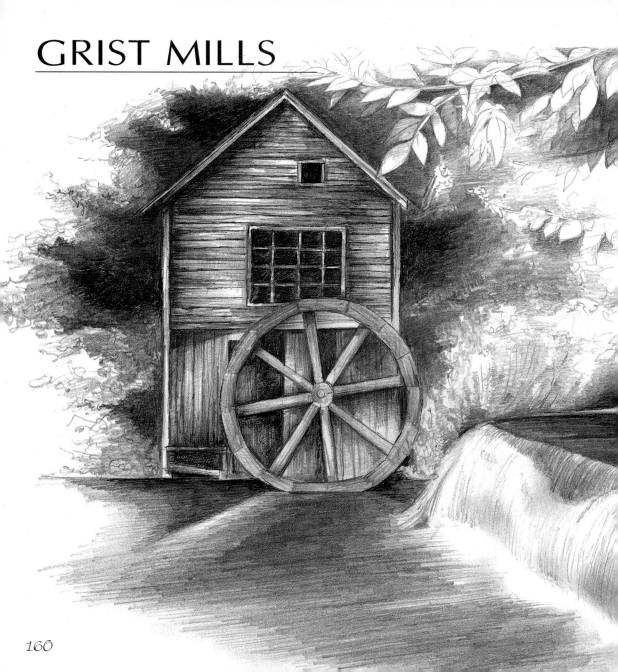

$\mathcal{M}ills$ were a community institution. Settlers needed them to convert the grain that they raised into flour or into feed. In the 1860s, when Wisconsin was a prime wheat-growing state, flour was shipped from Wisconsin mills to Eastern cities. In the 20th century, excess power from the mill's turbines was harnessed to generate electricity in some communities. Millponds were also important and useful. In addition to being popular spots for fishing and ice-skating, they supplied water to fight fires and, before the invention of electric refrigerators, provided villagers with ice.

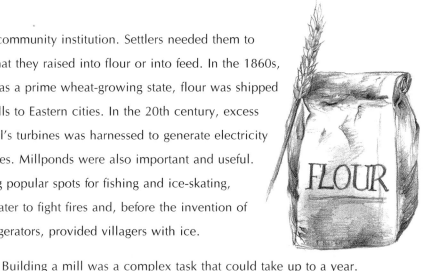

Building a mill was a complex task that could take up to a year. The millwright had to be an engineer and a carpenter, as well as a miller. To build a water-powered grain mill, the millwright had to locate a stream with sufficient water, construct a dam and a building, and fashion a system of gears and millstones. When you find such a mill, you'll see that it was built with a deep foundation. This was done so that even if the dam washed away in a flood, the mill would still stand. A deep foundation also enabled the mill to withstand vibrations caused by its heavy machinery.

# STANDS & SHANTIES

## Fishing shanties

When the lakes freeze, fishermen haul out their ice shanties.
These little buildings can be quite comfortable, stocked with chairs
and stoves. Usually, the angler with an ice shanty is fishing for panfish.

## Migrant worker housing

Migrant workers from south Texas come to Wisconsin in the summer to work in vegetable
fields. Many are housed in migrant worker camps like this one south of Montello.

## Deer stands

Some hunters prefer to sit or
stand about 10 feet off the ground
in deer stands while waiting for their
prey to walk underneath them. Look
for platforms wedged into trees or
freestanding buildings on stilts.

## school bus shelters

Parents in rural areas sometimes build small shelters
in which their children can wait for the school bus on cold mornings.
You will always find them alongside the road at the end of the drive.

163

Roadside
Flowers

# ROADSIDE FLOWERS

## Using This Guide

We've made no attempt to include every wildflower seen alongside Wisconsin's highways, but we have included the most common. Not all species are found throughout the state, however. Some, such as leadplant and blazing star prefer the dry, sandy soils of central Wisconsin; others, such as mayapple and trillium, like rich, moist soil. Still others like their feet wet; marsh marigold and wild iris, for example, grow in marshes. To help you identify a flower, we've noted where it grows, along with the season in which it blossoms.

With each flower illustration, we've provided the common as well as the scientific name. The scientific name is included because some common wildflowers have more than one common name. In some instances, two wildflowers share the same common name. For instance, people in Wisconsin often call wild columbine (*Aguilegia canadensis*) honeysuckle. Wild columbine grows 2 to 3 feet tall, and has delicate blossoms with upward pointing tubes. Honeysuckle (*Lonicera tatarica*) is more accurately the common name for a tall-growing shrub with red berries that is found in much of the state.

## Flowers and Farmsteads

Roadside flowers, besides being beautiful, can provide historic clues. Two common roadside plants, lilacs and orange daylilies, mark where a farmstead may once have stood. Neither of these plants are native to Wisconsin. They came west with the pioneers. Once the log cabin was up, a few daylily roots were planted on the sunny south side of the cabin, along with a few lilac plants. Both kinds of plants thrived, and neither required any care. In May, the lilacs sent forth their aromatic purple blossoms, and by July the orange daylilies were in full bloom, adding a splash of color to a pioneer's harsh life. Today, it is often only the lilacs and daylilies that remain as reminders of this earlier time.

## Weeds and Flowers

When is a plant a wildflower and when is it a weed? A weed is often defined as a plant out of place, regardless of whether or not it is nice to look at. Take the Canada thistle, for example. Examine it closely and you'll see a thing of beauty. Yet, ask any farmer what he thinks about thistles and he'll tell you how much he hates them. These spiny plants have no place in his field. (As an aside, the thistle is the Scottish national insignia. It seems that an army of barefoot Danish troops once attacked a Scotch stronghold that was surrounded by fields of thistles. The Danes stepped on the thistles and their yowling awakened the Scots, who defeated the invaders.)

But weeds can have redeeming uses. Most homeowners consider the dandelion to be a weed, and they spend many hours each spring digging, spraying and cursing it. Yet, the dandelion is often the first flower of spring, sending up its yellow head to remind us that winter is past. Dandelion plants can be made into wine, the leaves can be eaten as salad, and the roots can be boiled as a vegetable. For some people, chicory is a weed, yet it adds color to many roadsides from June through October—few wildflowers match its blue hue. Chicory leaves are sometimes made into salad, and its root, dried and roasted, is widely known as a coffee additive or substitute. The vigorous root also allows the plant to withstand hot summer days, and highway crews that attempt to mow it down have to return again and again.

Some truly handsome flowers have indeed become pests and have begun to crowd out other plant species. Purple loosestrife is one example. Introduced to North America from Europe in the mid-1800s, it has gradually spread westward, providing a splendid bloom of large magenta flowers on a tall spike. The flower was introduced by beekeepers because it is a good pollen plant. But because the plant has no natural enemies, it has taken over many wet areas.

On the other hand, some of the native wildflowers that we prize today were once despised. For instance, people used to believe that wild lupine robbed the soil of its nutrients. Its name comes from the Latin word *lupus*, meaning "wolf," an animal believed to be a wilderness robber. The logic was wrong in both respects. Wolves are not wilderness robbers, as naturalists have long known. And neither is the lupine a soil robber. Because it is a legume, it actually enriches the soil.

**Different flowers** bloom at different times and prefer different habitats—woods, water, fields, roadsides. To identify a species, consider first whether it is early (April to June) or late (July to September) in the growing season. Then notice the habitat. Beyond that, flower color and leaf shape are the easiest characteristics to determine from the road. Of the hundreds of flowers that bloom in Wisconsin, these are some of the most common roadside plants.

## Hawkweed
*Hieracium aurantiacum*
Red-orange flower heads on hairy stems. Hawkweed is also known as "devil's paintbrush".

## Dandelion
*Taxaxacum officinale*
Bright yellow flower, jagged leaves and a long, tenacious taproot.

## Mayapple
*Podophyllum peltatum*
White flower, hidden under large, umbrella-like leaves. Like most flowers on this page, mayapples are often found in large, showy masses.

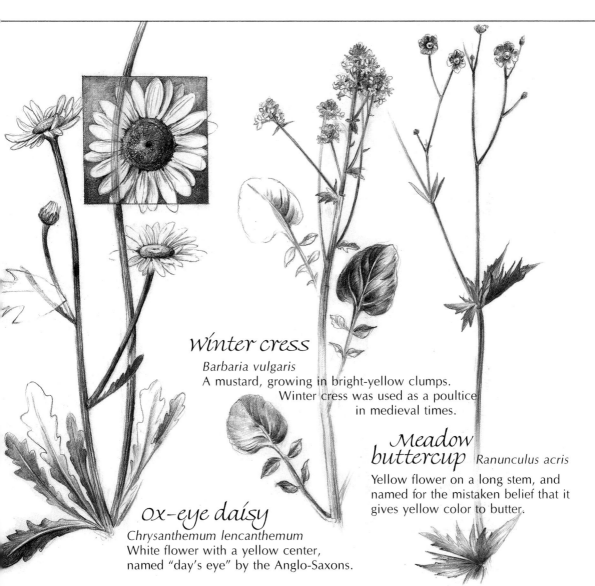

## winter cress
*Barbaria vulgaris*
A mustard, growing in bright-yellow clumps.
Winter cress was used as a poultice
in medieval times.

## Meadow
## buttercup *Ranunculus acris*
Yellow flower on a long stem, and
named for the mistaken belief that it
gives yellow color to butter.

## Ox-eye daisy
*Chrysanthemum lencanthemum*
White flower with a yellow center,
named "day's eye" by the Anglo-Saxons.

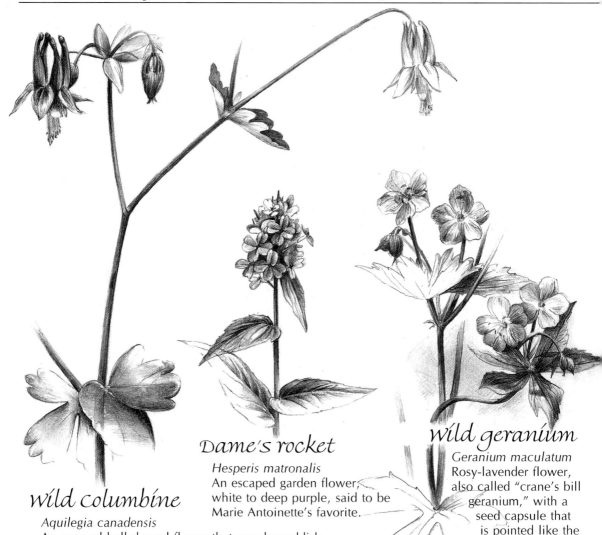

## wild columbine

*Aquilegia canadensis*
An unusual bell-shaped flower that may be reddish,
bluish or white. The name in Latin means "dovelike."

## Dame's rocket

*Hesperis matronalis*
An escaped garden flower,
white to deep purple, said to be
Marie Antoinette's favorite.

## wild geranium

*Geranium maculatum*
Rosy-lavender flower,
also called "crane's bill
geranium," with a
seed capsule that
is pointed like the
bill of a crane.

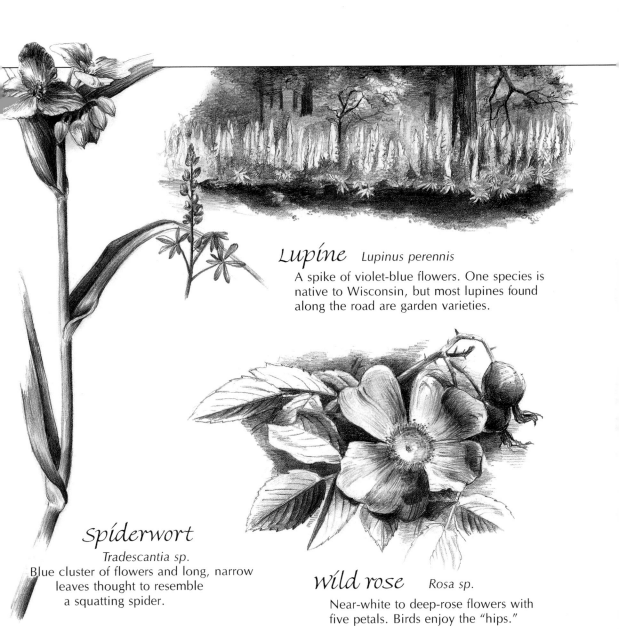

## Lupine  *Lupinus perennis*

A spike of violet-blue flowers. One species is native to Wisconsin, but most lupines found along the road are garden varieties.

## Spiderwort

*Tradescantia sp.*
Blue cluster of flowers and long, narrow leaves thought to resemble a squatting spider.

## Wild rose  *Rosa sp.*

Near-white to deep-rose flowers with five petals. Birds enjoy the "hips."

## Trillium

*Trillium grandiflorum*    White flower parts and leaves grow in threes—hence the name "trillium." These flowers are often seen carpeting a woods.

## Blue Flag    *Iris versicolor*

Swordlike leaves with conspicuous blue flowers. Roots are poisonous to cattle. Look for blue flags near water.

## Marsh Marigold

*Caltha palustris*

Golden-yellow flowers with large kidney-shaped leaves. As its name implies, this marigold grows near water.

## Thistle

*Cirsium spp.*
A weedy plant
with prickly leaves and seeds that are relished by goldfinches,
who also use the down for nests.

## Spotted knapweed

*Centaurea maculosa*
Straggly plants with lavender fringed
flowerheads. Knapweed looks somewhat
like a thistle but doesn't have prickles.

## Aster

*Aster sp.*
Colors vary, but clusters of daisylike flowers in late
summer are likely to be asters.

## Mullein

*Verbascum thapsus*
A tall, flowering stalk
and gray-green wooly
leaves, which Native
Americans used to
line footgear.

## Field goldenrod

*Solidago nemoralis*
Yellow flowers on a curving stem that is covered with fine gray hairs.

173

## Daylily
*Hemerocallis fulva*
Garden plants with showy orange
flowers, brought west by the pioneers.

## wild Parsnip
*Pastinaca sativa*
Tall, with a flat-topped
yellow flower cluster.
This is an Old World
garden parsnip, gone
wild. Its juice causes
a rash.

## Black-eyed Susan   *Rudbeckia hirta*
Bright-yellow flowers with a brown center.
The identity of "Susan" is not known.

## chicory

*Chicorium intybus*
A blue flower whose root
can be used to make a kind of
coffee. Chicory and Queen Anne's
lace often grow together.

## Queen Anne's lace

*Daucus carota*
Flat-topped white flower clusters with a red center said to
represent a drop of blood that fell from the queen's handmaiden
while she was making lace.

175

## Hairy vetch    *Vicia villosa*

Blue-flowered vines, often planted by road crews to control erosion.

## Birds-foot trefoil    *Lotus corniculatus*

Yellow to deep-orange flowers with leaves that appear to be in three parts but are in five. Birds-foot trefoil vines help prevent erosion.

## Yellow goatsbeard    *Tragopogon dubius*

A yellow flower and a large dandelionlike seedhead. The flower faces the sun in the morning and closes by midday.

### Milkweed    *Tragopogon dubius*

A tall plant with mauve flowers in a ball-like cluster and with a distinctive pod. The plant is the chief food of the larvae of monarch butterflies.

### Fireweed    *Epilobium augustifolium*

A tall plant with purple flowers that grows in clearings and burned-over areas.

### white water lily
*Nymphaea odorata*
Thick, platter-shaped leaves with a white flower that opens in the morning. Both the leaves and the flower float on the surface of the water.

### cow parsnip
*Heracleum lanatum*
A member of the same family as Queen Anne's lace, but a giant plant growing in moist areas, with flat white flower clusters up to 8 inches wide.

## Yellow pond lily

*Nuphar advena*
This plant, with yellow
flowers and broad leaves,
is also known as spatterdock.
The flowers and leaves float
on the surface of the water or
are raised slightly above it.

## Purple loosestrife

*Lythrum salicaria*
A nuisance weed with
purple flowers that displaces
other vegetation. It is illegal
to cultivate or distribute
purple loosestrife.

# Roadside Animals & Birds

# ROADSIDE ANIMALS & BIRDS

## *Wild Animals*

White-tailed deer are the most loved and most disliked wild animals in Wisconsin. There are more white-tailed deer today than when white settlers arrived. Deer are found everywhere in the state—more in the south than in the north—during all seasons, and can be seen any time of the day, although early evening is the best viewing time. Deer are beautiful, graceful animals with long ears, big brown eyes and a long white tail that flies up like a flag when the animal senses danger. But deer destroy field crops and can ruin orchards and Christmas tree plantations. Some 400,000 Wisconsin deer collide with cars each year, a situation that injures people, wrecks autos and usually kills the animal. Most car-deer collisions occur at night when the animals freely roam. Their eyes reflect headlights and give you some warning. But if you see a deer crossing the road, slow down; more are probably following.

If you spot a fawn (they have white spots on a brown coat) alongside the road, don't assume its mother has abandoned it. The doe is usually close by. Look at but don't touch the fawn.

Raccoons are also another very common sight at night. With their black masks and ringed tails, they are easy animals to identify. Your lights will reflect the raccoon's eyes. The skunk is often visible along Wisconsin's roads at night too. A skunk is black with white stripes down its back. If challenged, it will respond by spraying a liquid with an unforgettable, lingering smell. A skunk can spray its smelly liquid more than a dozen feet. Keep your family dog away from skunks. Many a naive dog that has encountered a skunk returns to its master with an aroma that lingers. A tomato-juice bath helps cut the stench.

One of Wisconsin's most distinctive animals is the porcupine, which is found in the northern third of the state. You'll know a porcupine by its quills—each animal may have up to 30,000. A porcupine doesn't shoot its quills as folklore suggests. If startled, the animal raises its quills until it looks like a living pin cushion. Each quill has a tiny fishhooklike barb at the end of it, making it difficult to remove. Keep an eye out for porcupines when you are camping. They crave salt and often will eat camping equipment that has been soaked with sweat, such as tool handles, ropes and gloves.

The red fox is a resident of the fence row, where it hunts for mice, cottontail rabbits and ruffed grouse. Although called a "red" fox, these animals come in a variety of colors, ranging from light blonde to a deep russet red. Doglike in appearance, red fox have a distinctive bushy tail, always tipped with white. They are fast runners, and you'll often glimpse them dashing across the road. Fox pairs mate for life. Usually three to 10 kits are born in April in an elaborate underground den. Occasionally, on the side of a hill you'll see a hole with dirt piled nearby. Chances are good that it's a fox den. The gray fox also resides in Wisconsin, most commonly in the south. Its coat is salt-and-pepper gray with orange and white markings. Because the gray fox is not as curious as the red fox, it is less frequently seen.

Identifying wild animal tracks in snow can be an interesting wintertime activity. When the snow is deep, deer travel on trails that cross roads from time to time. Their tracks are easily identified—look for hooves with two parts. Rabbits make large, oblong tracks with their hind feet, and smaller, round tracks with their front feet. Raccoon tracks look like small human hands and feet. A fox track is like a small dog's track, except that each footprint is spaced evenly one behind the other.

## Roadside Birds

Different birds tend to hang out in different places. Some are most commonly spotted flying, others are usually seen hopping on the ground, and still others might be perched on utility wires and wire fences. Which birds you see also depends on the season and where you are in the state. Many of Wisconsin's birds, especially songbirds, migrate to warmer parts of the world before winter sets in. Others move only from northern Wisconsin to the southern counties.

The robin, with its orange breast, is one of Wisconsin's most common birds and one of the first birds to return in spring. "Have you seen a robin yet?" is a question

Wisconsin people begin asking in March.

The bluebird is another beloved Wisconsin bird. Fortunately, its numbers are increasing. Through the efforts of environmental groups and interested citizens, there are now bluebird houses along many of Wisconsin's highways. You'll see bluebirds, with sky-blue backs and orange breasts, sitting on their houses or on wire fences. They, like the robin, return to the state early in the spring. Don't confuse bluebirds with tree swallows who compete for the same houses. Tree swallows have steely-blue to greenish-black backs, and their undersides are clear-white.

Among Wisconsin's most interesting birds is the cowbird, black with a brownish head. Cowbirds are villains in bird land. The female cowbird lays her eggs in other birds' nests, leaving the hatching to the other mother bird. Once out of the egg, the young cowbird is often the largest bird in the nest, crowding out its nest mates when they compete for food. You'll see adult cowbirds on fences and electric lines.

The blue jay is one of the state's year-round residents. It is conspicuously blue with white and black markings and has a head crest. Blue jays can be more than 12 inches long with a wingspread of more than 17 inches. In winter, the blue jay's striking colors are a welcome contrast to the drabness of the season. But the blue jay is also a villain that robs the nests of other birds and destroys the eggs.

Another all-season resident is the cardinal. The male cardinal is easy to identify, stunning red in color with some black around its bill and a prominent head crest. Females are yellowish-brown with some red; they also have a crest. Males are about 9 inches long with a wingspread of 12 inches and a 4-inch tail. Females are slightly smaller. Look for cardinals in pine thickets or small trees alongside the road.

One of the largest birds you'll see is the wild turkey. It can be spotted in the southern half of Wisconsin, in all seasons of the year. Wild turkeys are magnificent birds with glossy brown feathers and pale, bluish heads. Once almost gone from the state, they are now quite plentiful, thanks to the state's reintroduction efforts.

If you are near wetlands, keep an eye out for the impressive sandhill crane. These birds have grayish feathers and a red blotch above their eyes and stand 3 to 4 feet tall. Their wings span 6 to 7 feet. Sandhill cranes make a loud, prehistoric call unlike anything made by any other creature.

Also be on the lookout for bald eagles, whose numbers have increased dramatically in Wisconsin. Look for them in winter near the Wisconsin River dam at Prairie du Sac, and on the Mississippi River near Genoa. In summer, in northern Wisconsin, you'll often see one sitting high up in a tree, its distinctive white head reflecting the sunlight.

# ANIMALS *of the woods, fields & roadsides*

Wild animals inhabit all of Wisconsin's woods and fields. Sometimes you will spot them standing or scampering alongside the road. Other times, they are half-hidden. Stay alert, and look for movement in the grass or brush.

## Eastern chipmunk

Has stripes on its head, sides and back. Extensive burrows hold up to half a bushel of nuts.

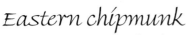

## Thirteen-lined ground squirrel

Coat has a "stars-and-stripes" pattern. Active during the day, these squirrels retreat to burrows at night.

## Woodchuck

Also known as a groundhog. Often seen sunbathing on top of its burrow.

## Gray squirrel

Usually gray on its back and sides and whitish below, with a large, bushy tail.

## Red squirrel

Rusty above and whitish below, with a harsh, strident call. A red squirrel is smaller than a gray squirrel.

# Porcupine

During the day, the
porcupine appears
as a round, dark
shape high in
a tree. It feeds
on buds, twigs
and bark at night.

# Red fox

Reddish on its back and face, white
underneath. The red fox is usually
seen in early morning and late afternoon.

# Eastern cottontail

Short-eared and with a short
white tail that's conspicuous
when it's running.

# white-tailed deer

The most abundant hoofed
mammal in North America,
with a tail distinctively white
on the underside, which it
raises when alarmed.

# ANIMALS *found near water*

## Muskrat

Much smaller than a beaver and with a narrow tail. Muskrat lodges are made of grasses and sedges and are smaller than those made by beavers.

## Beaver

North America's largest rodent, with a paddlelike tail and prominent front teeth used for gnawing down trees. Beaver lodges are made of sticks and mud.

## Raccoon

Easily identified by its "mask" and bushy ringed tail. Raccoons will eat almost any type of food.

## Striped skunk

Unmistakable with its white stripe. If a skunk arches its back and raises its tail, get out of the way or face the smelly consequences.

## Deer mouse

Resembles a deer only in the dark-above, light-below pattern of its fur. This commonly found creature is active year-round.

## Opossum

Has a long, pinkish nose in a white face and 50 teeth—more than any other North American land mammal. The opossum is our only pouched mammal.

# BIRDS *of the fields & edges*

Like wild animals, different birds live in different habitats, according to where they will likely find their preferred foods and nesting sites. Usually, male birds are more easily identified than females because their color and markings are more distinctive.

## Killdeer

Look for two black bars across the upper chest and a white collar. Listen for a loud, ringing call.

## Turkey

Has made a successful comeback in Wisconsin. Turkeys roost in trees but are frequently seen in small flocks along the roadside. Males display their tails during the breeding period.

## Goldfinch

Males are bright yellow with a black forehead, wings and tail; females are olive-green. Goldfinches are often seen in small flocks singing *per-chick-o-rees!*

## Snow bunting

Takes on a brownish tinge in winter, when large flocks are seen swirling over snowy fields. Look for their white wing patches.

## Ring-necked pheasant

A game species introduced into North America. Males have a long, sweeping, pointed tail and, ususally, a white neck-ring.

## Horned lark

A brown bird that walks—rather than hops—on the ground and, when flying, folds its wings after every beat. Males have black sideburns and black horns, the latter not always noticeable.

## Rose-breasted grosbeak

Males have a rose breast patch and a black and white pattern on their backs and wings. Both males and females incubate the eggs.

*Red breast*

## cedar waxwing

Soft brown in color, with a black face pattern and yellow-tipped tail. These sociable birds often travel in groups and may be seen passing berries from beak to beak.

## cardinal

Males are unmistakable, flame-red in color with a distinct crest and heavy bill. Females are a duller cinnamon-yellow, but are similarly shaped. Listen for a loud, clear whistle.

## Blue jay

Sky-blue feathers with black and white stripes and patches, and a trademark crest. The blue jay is a bully and will heckle large and small birds, and even cats.

## Red-headed Woodpecker

Our only woodpecker with an entirely red head. The back is solid black, and the rump and wing patches are white. A stiff tail keeps the bird propped up on tree trunks where it feeds on insects.

## Common grackle

Males are glossy black, with a purple, bronze or greenish sheen. Their unusually long, diamond-shaped tails distinguish them from other black birds. When grackles flock, the noise can be deafening.

orange

## Baltimore oriole

Males are flaming orange and black with a black head. Their song is a rich whistle.

## Flicker

A member of the woodpecker family, with a brown back and a white rump. Males have a black mustache.

# BIRDS *found near water*

### Blue-winged teal

Blue

A small duck with a white crescent on its face and a blue patch on its wing.

### Mallard

The most common duck in the world. The male's head and neck are glossy green, with a white ring.

### Wood duck

A crested head and white throat and facial pattern. Females nest in tree cavities or in manmade boxes.

### Great blue heron

A large blue-gray bird with a long neck and bill that it uses to spear fish. The heron flies with its head and neck folded back.

### Canada goose

Our most common goose, with a dark neck, back and tail and a white area on its cheek.

## Common loon

Easily identified by its black and white pattern and a wild, yodeling cry. Loons, able to swim underwater for long distances, can seem to "disappear" into a lake.

## Herring gull

Often called a seagull but lives close to fields as often as to coasts. Adults have a white breast and head and a gray back.

## Coot

A black bird with a band of shining white that covers its bill and runs up its forehead. The coot bobs its head when it swims.

## Sandhill crane

Tall gray bird with a reddish cap. Its wingspan is larger than that of the great blue heron, and it flies with a straight neck. Both males and females are spectacular dancers during courtship.

## Green heron

A small heron with a bluish back, brown neck and greenish-yellow legs. When alarmed, it will stretch its neck and display a shaggy crest.

195

# BIRDS *seen on fences & utility wires*

## American kestrel

A small, footlong falcon, with a pinkish-brown back and a mustached face. Males have blue-gray wings. You'll see kestrels hovering with rapidly beating wings while looking for prey.

## Belted kingfisher

Blue-gray with a big crested head and large bill. Watch it hover and plunge for prey with a rattling call.

## Red-winged blackbird

Males are black with a red and yellow shoulder patch. These birds feed and roost in flocks, except during late summer when they hide in the marshes to grow new feathers.

*Red & yellow patch*

## Meadowlark

Gray-brown with a bright yellow breast and a black crescent. A diminishing species as our prairies and meadows disappear.

## Song sparrow

Plain brownish bird with three dots in a triangle on its streaked throat and breast. Listen for a cheerful song: "*Tea-tea-tea! Polly put the kettle on!*"

## House sparrow

A bird that was brought here from England a century ago and has stolen many of the bluebird's nesting sites. Males have a large black bib.

## Eastern kingbird

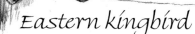

Dark gray above and clear white underneath with a white band across the tip of its tail. The kingbird takes its name from its habit of heckling other birds.

## Mourning dove

Slim, grayish-brown body with scattered brown spots and a long, pointed tail. Listen for its soft *coo-coo-coo*.

## Tree swallow

Glossy blue-black with a slightly forked tail.
Will nest in birdhouses and mailboxes as well as in trees.

## Eastern bluebird

Males are bright blue with an orange-red throat and breast. Bluebird numbers declined when foreign birds took over their tree holes, but now are up, thanks to specially built nesting boxes.

## Robin

Males are dark gray with a brick-red breast. The robin is an enthusiastic singer with a loud, caroling song.

## Indigo bunting

Males are indigo-blue, with blackish wings and tail. The indigo bunting is one of the few birds that sings heartily at midday.

# BIRDS *often seen flying*

## American crow

All black—body, wings, head, beak and feet.
Crows are disliked by farmers, whose cornfields they
raid. They also eat slugs and caterpillars, along with
the eggs and young of other birds.

## Raven

All black like a crow but much
larger—two feet long—and more
solitary. The call is different too:
A crow *caws*, a raven croaks
*cr-r-ruck*.

## Barn swallow

Nest in barns, silos and woodsheds. These swallows have a deeply forked tail with outer feathers that stick out like wires.

## Red-tailed hawk

An easy hawk to identify with a tail that is brick-red on its upper surface. A soaring red-tail is usually looking for a mouse supper.

## Bald eagle

Mature birds have a white head and tail. Young birds are completely dark brown. You'll see bald eagles up north in summer, and along the Lower Wisconsin and Mississippi rivers in winter.

199

# FOR FURTHER READING

### The Landscape

Curtis, John T. *The Vegetation of Wisconsin*. Madison, WI: The University of Wisconsin Press, 1959, 1971.

Gard, Robert E. and Sorden, L. G. *Romance of Wisconsin Place Names*. Madison, WI: Wisconsin House, 1968.

Holmes, Fred L. *Old World Wisconsin*. Minocqua, WI: NorthWord Press, Inc., 1944, 1990.

Martin, Lawrence. *The Physical Geography of Wisconsin*. Madison, WI: The University of Wisconsin Press, 1965.

Nesbit, Robert C. *Wisconsin, A History*. (2nd ed.) Madison, WI: The University of Wisconsin Press, 1989.

Risjord, Norman K. *Wisconsin: The Story of the Badger State*. Madison, WI: Wisconsin Trails, 1995.

Schultz, Gwen. *Wisconsin's Foundations: A Review of the State's Geology and Its Influence on Geography and Human Activity*. Dubuque, Iowa: Kendall/Hunt, 1986.

Smith, Alice E. *The History of Wisconsin, Vol. 1, From Exploration to Statehood*. Madison, WI: State Historical Society of Wisconsin, 1973.

Wisconsin Legislative Reference Bureau. *State of Wisconsin: 1995-1996 Blue Book*. Madison, WI: Joint Committee on Legislative Organization, State of Wisconsin, 1995.

### The Farmstead

Apps, Jerry. *Barns of Wisconsin*. Madison, WI: Wisconsin Trails, 1977, 1995.

Arthur, Eric and Dudley Witney. *The Barn: A Vanishing Landmark in North America*. Greenwich, CT: New York Graphic Society Ltd., 1972.

Harris, Bill. *Barns of America*. New York: Crescent Books, 1991.

Noble, Allen G. and Wilhelm, Hubert G. H. (eds.) *Barns of the Midwest*. Athens, Ohio: Ohio University Press, 1995.

Schuler, Stanley. *American Barns, In a Class by Themselves*. Exton, PA: Schiffer Publishing, 1984.

Sloane, Eric. *An Age of Barns*. New York: Funk & Wagnalls, 1967.

### Farm Animals

Edwards, Elwyn Hartley. *Horses*. New York: Darling Kindersley, 1993.

Rath, Sara. *About Cows*. Ashland, WI: NorthWord, 1987.

### Other Rural Buildings

Apps, Jerry. *Breweries of Wisconsin*. Madison, WI: University of Wisconsin Press, 1992.

Apps, Jerry. *Mills of Wisconsin and the Midwest*. Madison, WI: Wisconsin Trails, 1980.

Apps, Jerry. *One-Room Country Schools*. Amherst, WI: Amherst Press, 1996.

## Roadside Flowers

Edsall, Marian S. *Roadside Plants and Flowers: A Traveler's Guide to the Midwest and Great Lakes Area*. Madison, WI: University of Wisconsin Press, 1985.

Good, Mary B. *Trillium: A Guide to the Common Wildflowers of Northeastern Wisconsin*. Woodruff, WI: Jober Productions, 1990.

Niering, William and Olmstead, Nancy C. *The Audubon Society Field Guide to North American Wildflowers, Eastern Region*. New York: Alfred A. Knopf, 1979.

Peterson, Roger Tory and McKenny, Margaret. *A Field Guide to Wildflowers of Northeastern and North-Central North America*. Boston: Houghton Mifflin, 1968.

Courtenay, Booth and Zimmerman, James H. *Wildflowers and Weeds*. New York: Van Hostrand Reinhold Company.

## Roadside Animals and Birds

Burt, W. H. and Grossenheider, R. P. *A Field Guide to the Mammals*. Boston: Houghton Mifflin, 1952, 1961.

Gromme, Owen J. *Birds of Wisconsin*. Madison, WI: University of Wisconsin Press, 1963, 1974.

Judd, Mary K. *Wisconsin Wildlife Viewing Guide*. Helena, MT: Falcon Press, 1995.

Kochanoff, Peggy. *A Field Guide to Nearby Nature*. Missoula, MT: Mountain Press Publishing Company, 1994.

Robbins, Samual D. *Wisconsin Birdlife*. Madison, WI: University of Wisconsin Press, 1991.

Stokes, Donald W. *A Guide to Nature in Winter*. Boston: Little, Brown, 1976.

Wernert, Susan (ed.). *North American Wildlife*. Pleasantville, NY: Reader's Digest Association, 1982.

Whitaker, John O. *National Audubon Society Field Guide to North American Mammals*. New York: Alfred A. Knopf, 1980, 1994.

Jackson, Hartley H.T. *Mammals of Wisconsin*. Madison, WI: University of Wisconsin Press, 1961.

Peterson, Roger Tory. *A Field Guide to the Birds East of the Rockies*. Boston: Houghton Mifflin, 1980.

# INDEX

# INDEX

# INDEX

# More Books on Wisconsin
## from Wisconsin Trails

### Barns of Wisconsin
*by Jerry Apps*

### Mills of Wisconsin
*by Jerry Apps and Allen Strang*

### Great Wisconsin Walks
*by Wm. Chad McGrath*

### County Parks of Wisconsin
*by Jeannette and Chet Bell*

### Great Weekend Adventures
*from the Editors of Wisconsin Trails*

### Best Wisconsin Bike Trips
*by Phil Van Valkenberg*

### Best Canoe Trails of Southern Wisconsin
*by Michael E. Duncanson*

### Great Golf in Wisconsin
*by John Hughes and Jeff Mayers*

### Wisconsin, The Story of the Badger State
*by Norman K. Risjord*

## Wisconsin Trails
P.O. Box 5650 • Madison, WI 53705 • (800) 236-8088